The Westchester Review

A LITERARY JOURNAL OF WRITERS FROM THE HUDSON TO THE SOUND

THE WESTCHESTER REVIEW

FOUNDER AND PUBLISHER
JoAnn Duncan Terdiman

EDITOR IN CHIEF EMERITA
Louise Albert

MANAGING EDITOR
Naomi L. Lipman

ADMINISTRATIVE COORDINATOR
Randi Kaplan

EDITORIAL BOARD
Stephanie Kaplan Cohen
Judith Naomi Fish
Lesleigh Forsyth
Ruth Obernbreit
Amy Ralston Seife

ADVISORY EDITOR
Rachel Simon

CONSULTANTS
Mary Anne Borowka
Susan Gale Duncan
Bob Glass
George Gottlieb
Ann Spindel
Paul Spindel
Rick Wingate

ART DIRECTOR
Orlando Adiao

The Westchester Review is published annually. The editors welcome previously unpublished stories, poetry, and nonfiction by established and emerging writers living, working, or studying in New York State's Westchester County.

We accept up to two prose pieces (not to exceed 5,000 words each) or up to five poems, per author. Manuscripts must be typed double-spaced and be accompanied by a self-addressed stamped envelope for reply purposes only. Submissions will not be returned. If you want us to acknowledge receipt of your work, include a self-addressed stamped postcard. Electronic submissions may be sent to *submissions@westchesterreview.com*.

Manuscripts should be sent to
The Westchester Review
P.O. Box 246H
Scarsdale, NY 10583

For more information, visit our Web site (*www.westchesterreview.com*).

Library of Congress Control Number: 2006908683

ISBN: 978-0-615-34995-4

CONTENTS

PROSE

POETRY

Igloo

Alana Ruprecht

DELPHINE CAME BY AT THE END OF OCTOBER TO TELL ME THAT she and Henry were moving back to France. She spoke in her usual manner, telling me all of this in the same way she might say they were walking down to the river to feed the ducks or going to Block Island for the weekend, as if it were nothing out of the ordinary.

"I was hoping," she said, "that you might want Babu." Despite her casual way of asking, I had the impression this was more than a request.

Babu was a guinea pig. I hadn't grown up with animals and I didn't know what to do with them. What little I knew about pets was that, sooner or later, they got sick, died, or ran away. And the people, the ones who had cared for them, could grieve for days. I didn't really want a guinea pig, but I liked Delphine, and I liked Henry, her son, and now that they were moving, the truth was I wanted the things that had belonged to them. Without exactly saying yes or no, I found myself agreeing to take the guinea pig.

"Of course, we'd give you his cage and food," she said. "And any of our furniture or plants you want, help yourself. We're not taking anything."

Delphine and Henry lived in the apartment next to mine. She had invited me over for coffee on occasion. I found out, on one of my first visits, that we listened to the same classical radio station, and I was filled with a giddy contentedness to know that we had something, if only that, in common. Besides living in the same apartment building, we had seemed, until that discovery, to diverge at every possible meeting point: I was a receptionist at a chiropractic office; she had the means to stay at home with her son. I was slightly overweight and dissatisfied with my hair color; she was tall and slim and had dark-brown hair that curled neatly under her chin. I was from Dobbs Ferry and—my god!—she was French.

She had lived most of her life in New York so her accent was nearly unnoticeable to me. I had never known anyone from France before and any impressions I had had about French women from movies or books vanished when I met Delphine. She struck me as being wholly uninterested in what people thought of her. She dressed in long, flowy skirts and big, complicated sweaters. She was an artist and, most days, if it wasn't raining or snowing, she sat outside the apartment building and painted while Henry played in the yard.

Henry was four, spoke French and English, and liked to collect snails. He brought them inside in buckets and put them on the stairs and banisters, where they left trails on the wood as they moved to places they never should have gone. He kept some of them as pets in a shoebox. He told me once that he had named one Willa, after me, but that it had disappeared. I laughed because Delphine had laughed, but the comment worried me, not out of concern for the snail, but for myself. I was mildly superstitious, and so I promptly tried to forget it and chalk it up to the active imagination of a four-year-old. Delphine didn't mind the snails—in fact, she encouraged Henry and provided him with the buckets in the first place. She told me that she wanted to support all of his passions, something her parents had not done for her.

Often, I thought what a lucky coincidence it was to live next door to Delphine. Even going into her apartment gave me a sense of what her life was like and, perhaps, what mine could be like. It was filled with beautiful furniture, all made from the same type of dark wood. Everything she owned looked like it had been carefully chosen, from the cream-colored sofa to the small writing table by the window that supported an assortment of neatly stacked letters and books. Paintings—some by Henry, the rest, I imagined, by Delphine—hung on the walls. In every room she had fresh flowers—not in vases, but in pitchers and watering cans.

Then there was my apartment. It told nothing of travels to France or anywhere far away, since I had never traveled farther than Maine. Instead, it was filled with furniture I had acquired haphazardly or been given, and none of it matched. Most of it was made of particleboard. But each piece served its purpose—the table had legs, the chairs had backs, the dresser had drawers. Someday, because all of it was temporary—my job, my apartment, my furniture, my life—these possessions would be replaced with things much better, finer, grander. At least, that's what I hoped. I felt, at times, as if I were still a young girl, drawing the outline of a house, then the roof, and the people inside.

At Delphine's, our attention was usually turned to Henry, who would be playing with the snails or Babu. Babu's cage was in the living room, and Henry would sit by the cage petting—or pestering—Babu. Babu had a black face, black rump, and orange middle, like a giant caterpillar. "He's the king of the castle," Henry liked to say. The "castle" was actually a small pink plastic igloo, just big enough for a guinea pig to hide in. Delphine told me that Henry had spotted it at a pet store and insisted that Babu must have it, and she had indulged him. Besides snails, Henry was interested in all things medieval, which to him meant kings and dragons and castles. Babu became King Babu, and the snails were often dragons come to invade the castle. The snails would sometimes be forgotten and die in the cage.

The igloo summed up what attracted me the most to Delphine's apartment: being in her rooms made you feel as if you were somewhere else entirely—France or, for Henry, medieval times, or, in the case of Babu, the Arctic. Everyone had the necessary objects to shelter them from the place they really were. I wanted an igloo of my own.

Our conversations didn't extend to our personal lives. I didn't talk about mine because there wasn't much to say or, rather, much that I could bring myself to say. Delphine never mentioned the man, Adam. I only knew his name because the walls were thin and I had heard her call him that.

Adam came over once or twice a week to see Henry, and they played together in the yard. I came home from work at about the same time Adam usually showed up for Henry, and I'd pass them outside or on the stairs. Henry would say hello and invite me to play with them, and Adam would flash an uncertain smile my way. I'd attempt to smile in return—though if I'd had a mirror, I think I would have seen that the corners of my mouth didn't turn up enough to be called any such thing—and hurry on. Adam was tall and, though he was attractive enough to have once been a fitting counterpart to Delphine, he had a hunched stance, as if waiting to be tackled by some unseen opponent.

One night, I heard them arguing. Delphine sounded frantic and angry. His voice was loud and low, like someone talking on the radio with the volume turned up. I had been working on a crossword puzzle and put my pencil down. I froze and listened.

"Don't wake Henry," Delphine said. "Let's talk about this another time."

He said something in reply, and then I heard Henry crying and screaming. I briefly considered doing something—perhaps knocking on the door—but I was afraid. I didn't want Delphine to think I had been eavesdropping. Besides, I didn't think Delphine was in any danger, so when the argument reached a point where things were neither improving nor worsening, I went to my bedroom, the room farthest away from them, put ear plugs in, and went back to my crossword puzzle.

It wasn't too long after that when Delphine told me they were moving, and then, a week later, she and Henry came by to drop off Babu and the plants. They showed up at my door, Delphine holding the cage, Henry clinging to her leg. His face was red, fresh with tears. Delphine set Babu's cage in my living room, and I carried the plants in.

"There," Delphine said. "Look how happy he is already."

Whether Babu was happy or not, I couldn't tell. He was inside the igloo, as usual. Henry approached the cage and seemed to be on the verge of cheering up as he stuck his hand in the igloo, but then he crumpled up, hiding his face and crying once more. "Babu," Henry said, pronouncing the name in a long, sorrowful manner. "I want King Babu."

"Babu has to stay here with Willa," Delphine said. "He can't go with us. Guinea pigs don't like to go on airplanes. They get scared."

Then she said, "We can get another guinea pig in France."

"But I want *him*," Henry said.

I felt I should say that I would take good care of him, but the moment came and went, and I didn't want to make a promise I wasn't sure was true.

"Why don't you blow Babu a kiss?" Delphine said.

Henry scrunched up close to the cage, peered into the igloo, and blew a kiss inside. "You forgot," he said. "Babu is scared of the dark."

"That's right," Delphine said, more seriously than anything else she had said up to this point. "He likes a night-light on."

When they left, I couldn't bring myself to let her know how sad I really was. In many ways, I'd hardly known her. Our goodbye was short and friendly, but with a certainty of never seeing each other again: her life would probably go one way and change into something new and beautiful, and mine, most inevitably, would stay the same. Delphine told me the name of the town they were moving to: Ramatuelle. I thought of telling her how lucky she was to be leaving, to have something to look forward to, but it was too difficult to get the words out of my mouth and so I just said goodbye.

After they were gone, I went back to her apartment to look around. The rooms felt deserted without her paintings and books. I took a few pieces of furniture that I could move myself—a writing table and a chest. The landlord, I guess, had agreed to keep or sell the rest of her belongings, due to her quick departure. Having her possessions made sense to me in a way having my own things didn't. They were the small interlocking pieces of a home that couldn't come apart.

As for Babu, he was afraid of me for the first few days and stayed in his igloo. He came out of the igloo only when he was hungry and then he circled his food bowl like a shark. He dragged the vegetables I gave him into the igloo to devour in private. Mostly I didn't have much to do with him—I simply fed him as Delphine had asked—and I think this suited us both fine. I imagine that he preferred to hide in his igloo rather than be petted and bothered. Having him was not as bad or complicated as I had thought it would be, and in a way, I got used to Babu.

A couple of weeks later, as I was coming home from work, I saw someone standing outside Delphine's door, in the shadows. From far away, I thought it might somehow be Delphine, come back from France! For a brief moment, I was hopeful and filled with anticipation. But when I got closer, I could see that it was not Delphine. It was Adam. I felt my stomach drop, and I dug deep in my purse for my keys.

"Good evening," he said.

I said hello, and then after considering the possibility that he might not know what had happened to Delphine and Henry, I said, "They moved."

"Yes," he said. "I know. Actually, I came to see you. May I come in?"

I dug deeper in my purse. I seemed to find everything but my keys—wallet, gum wrappers, receipts, eyeglass case. I knew there was no reason for Adam to be here. As for what he might want from me, I could come up with no good answer.

He continued. "I spoke to Delphine. She said you might have some of her things." He stood against the door in the same awkward way I'd noticed on previous occasions, though more pronounced now—his shoulders more hunched, his feet farther apart.

"Oh?" I said. I searched more frantically now, jingling the contents around in my purse. I kept finding my car keys. That he knew who I was seemed an invasion of privacy, a dismissal of the way things were, which was that he and I had nothing to do with each other.

"I believe you have something that's very important to me," he said. "I was hoping I could have it back. I'm certainly willing to pay you for it." He reached into his coat and produced a wallet stuffed with bills.

"Well, I only have a few of her things." Immediately, I wished I had lied. I didn't want to give him anything of Delphine's. I found the keys to my apartment—they had disappeared under the purse lining. And when I opened the door, as if I had agreed to his request, he followed me in.

"You have a nice place," he said.

"Thanks," I said. I knew that everything that was happening was all wrong. Deep inside me, an internal alarm bell was going off.

I didn't trust him. Maybe it was because I had heard them arguing, but all along, whenever I had seen Adam, there was something about him I didn't like.

"I know this must seem weird," he said, inspecting my apartment. "I don't normally do this. It's a strange situation, you know, one I hope you'll never be in. But they left." He paused and laughed gravely. "Well, you know they left. And now she tells me you have her things." Adam walked over to Babu's cage, lifted up the igloo and corralled Babu into the corner. Babu kicked his legs as Adam picked him up.

"Please don't pick him up," I said. "I don't think he likes it." Even though I had not had much to do with Babu since I'd had him, I felt protective of Delphine's things, including the guinea pig. I knew Delphine wouldn't have wanted him to have Babu—if she had, I reasoned, she would have offered him to Adam and not to me. My dislike of Adam grew and I found myself becoming angry and fearful of him being in my apartment.

"Nonsense," he said. "He likes it. It was kind of you to take care of Babu, but Delphine should have asked me. She shouldn't have inconvenienced you with this."

I wondered if this was how Adam had been with Delphine: quietly bullying.

"It's no inconvenience," I said. "I like him." And as I said it, I felt that I did indeed like Babu. I wanted to keep him for my own because he had been in Delphine's life and now he was part of mine.

"Babu belonged to my son," Adam said. He sat down on the sofa, Babu in his lap. In front of the sofa was Delphine's chest, which I used as a coffee table. There were deep carvings on the lid, which Adam seemed to be studying.

"This was ours, too," he said, gesturing to the chest. "I used to keep my sweaters in it."

The chest looked like an antique. Probably it was very valuable.

"Delphine gave that to me, too," I said, feeling strongly that I would have to be more forceful with him than I was used to being.

He laughed. "Don't worry, I don't want the furniture. I came for this."

I looked at Babu. He was gnawing on Adam's sweater sleeve. "I hope you don't mind," he said. "It was my son's pet, you understand."

"I do mind," I said. "Babu is mine now." I felt worried and sick to my stomach. I didn't know how it had happened that suddenly I seemed to be in the thick of Adam and Delphine's problems, and that their problems were becoming my own. All my life I had felt alone, but knowing Delphine, and now having her possessions and even her guinea pig, made me feel slightly less so.

"Here," Adam said. He pulled fifty dollars out of his wallet.

"I don't want it," I said, even though I could have used the money.

"A hundred," he said. "It's just a guinea pig. You can get another one at the pet store."

"I only want Babu," I said. "Delphine gave him to me."

"You don't understand. Babu belonged to my son, and my son is gone. Look, this shouldn't be difficult. Two hundred."

"No," I said. I looked at Babu squirming in Adam's arms. I wanted to rescue Babu, to put him back under the igloo where he'd be safe.

"This is ridiculous," Adam said. Something changed in his demeanor—he straightened up. The hunched posture was gone. "I'm taking him."

He clutched Babu in his arms, stood up, and headed for the door. Unable and unwilling to fight back, I grabbed the igloo and gave it to Adam.

"Take this," I said. "He needs it."

And then they were gone.

THERE WAS A SMALL PET STORE in the same shopping center as the chiropractic office where I worked. I had never been in it before but, after Adam took Babu, I felt compelled to go in. Guilt was taking hold of me for losing something that had belonged to Delphine.

The bells on the door jingled when I went in. The store was dark with a green fluorescence reflecting off the long rows of fish tanks and terrariums. Jumbo bags of food and bedding obstructed the aisles. A man with thinning brown hair appeared from behind the counter and asked if I needed any help.

"Do you have any guinea pigs?" I asked.

"I've got one," he said. "Been here a long time." He waited a moment, gauging, perhaps, if I had lost interest, and then he led me to a room in the back.

All along the wall cages were stacked, with hamsters, rats, mice, and a lone chinchilla. I peered in at the hamsters, which were sleeping in a pile on top of each other, some of their bodies squashed flat against the glass.

The guinea pig was in a cage on the floor. Wood shavings and hay covered the cage bottom. The guinea pig was orange, its hair arranged in whorls of rosettes. It hunched in the corner of the cage, looking at something, or nothing.

"Can I pick it up?" I asked.

"Be careful," he said. "They're squirrelly."

I reached in and caught hold of the guinea pig. It was soft and warm in my hands. Its eyes were so close together that they made it look cross-eyed.

"Strange little things, aren't they," he said.

"Yes," I said. "Very strange." I suddenly felt that I was in the wrong store, in the wrong place entirely. The room looked like a forgotten exhibit in the dark corner of a museum—all of the unwanted rodents on display, and all of the cages neatly stacked, as if their glass walls were mirrors, and the mirrors reflected our vulnerabilities and all the ways we had tried, and failed, to not be alone. ◇

Cutout Dolls

Judith Naomi Fish

H OW RELIGIOUS ARE THEY?" I ASK ETTI. I HAVE TO KNOW BEFORE
we start to play so we can figure out how the story goes.
Linda, Betsy, Diane, and Gloria are lying on my bedroom
carpet in a line. They're wearing bathing suits, every one a different
color, but soon we'll dress them up in their cutout-doll clothes and
probably have them go to school.

"They're Orthodox," Etti says. "Like us."

"I want Conservative," I tell her. "That way they can do more
things. Maybe even Reform." My heart beats fast when I say this.

"Not Reform!" Etti yells. "You want them to ride on *Shabbos?*"

She grabs Diane and Gloria, the dolls she brought with her up to
my apartment, and pulls their box of clothes closer to her crossed legs.
"I'm not playing if they're Reform. Even Conservative is too much.
Men and women sit together in *shul!*"

"So what?" I say. "Big deal. You think God doesn't hear them
because they sit together?"

I can see Etti's cheeks turning red.

"My father says *they* don't hear *God* because they're looking at each
other, the men and women, and they're not paying attention, so they
don't *daven*. That's what he says, and he's a rabbi."

"So make your dolls Orthodox," I tell her. "Linda and Betsy are
mine and they're going to be Conservative, and a little Reform, too."

"Well, Diane and Gloria aren't going to play with them," Etti says.

10

"Their parents won't let them." She takes a blue long-sleeve dress out of her box and puts it on Gloria. I watch her fold the tabs over Gloria's shoulders and look in the box for more clothes. "She's going to wear the red coat and the matching hat," Etti says. "She's going to *shul*. So is Diane."

"Who says it's *Shabbos?*" I ask her. "We haven't even decided yet the day of the week. My dolls are going to school, but they're getting out early today and then they're going to Brighton Beach. It's almost summer."

"It is not," Etti says. "Look: Diane and Gloria are both wearing coats and patent-leather shoes. They have on knee socks. It's the winter."

I watch the way the red on Etti's cheeks is spreading up to her eyes and over by her ears. It looks like someone has given her two smacks.

"You know what?" I tell her. "Let's have them all Orthodox—mine, too—but one day they decide to be a little Reform and after *shul* on *Shabbos* they get on the bus and go to Brighton Beach, just to see what would happen."

"My dolls aren't going to do that!" Etti shouts. "Are you crazy? Even *your* dolls wouldn't do that. Their parents would wonder where they were and they would kill them if they knew they rode the bus on *Shabbos*."

I put white shorts and sleeveless blouses on Linda and Betsy, and then *shul* clothes on top of those, and then winter coats over everything. There are a lot of tabs to fold over.

"This way they can go to *shul*," I say, "and no one will know what's underneath and that they're planning to go to the beach later. They're running away from home."

"They are not," Etti says. "Diane and Gloria are going to tell on them. They'll tell their father, who's a rabbi, and he'll tell Linda and Betsy's parents and they won't let them out of the house. Anyway, look what your dolls are wearing—you're making it winter and summer at the same time. You don't play right."

Everything Etti says is getting me really angry.

"Your dolls are going to tell on my dolls?" I ask her. "Who are they going to tell? We don't even have parent cutout dolls."

11

Etti digs into her box and pulls out Doris Day. "This is the mother." She holds her up and hangs the tabs of a black dress with a flared skirt from her shoulders. "And the mother is going to tell the father, who you can't see because he's in the bathroom now, and they're going to get your dolls in big trouble."

"I'm not playing cutout dolls with you anymore," I tell Etti. "All you want to do is fight and not have fun. Look how red your face is—go look in the mirror, you old boss!"

"I'm going home," Etti says. "I'm never coming up here to play with you again." She grabs her dolls and throws them in the box. Gloria's red matching hat flies up and lands on Linda's coat.

"Mine!" I yell, and grab it up with my dolls.

"Give that back!" Etti cries. "It's mine. It belongs to Gloria. It's part of her outfit."

She starts pulling at my dolls, at Linda's foot and Betsy's arm, and they tear off. I can't believe it. I hold on to my dolls with one hand and reach for Etti's box with the other. I dump everything out and now all the dolls are mixed up and Diane's clothes are torn and so are Gloria's, and Linda's and Betsy's too, and Etti is crying and so am I and my mother is at the bedroom door yelling—

"What is going on in here? What are you girls screaming about?" Then she looks at me. "I am never buying you another cutout doll book after seeing you fight like this."

"She broke my box!" Etti is really crying now. "She tore everything apart."

"You did it to me!" I'm crying back. "And you started. It's your fault because you wanted Orthodox. If they had been Reform it wouldn't have happened. They could have gone to the beach."

My mother grabs an empty paper bag from my closet and bends down to pick up all the cutout dolls. She stuffs them in the bag and then she and Etti march out of my room. I run to my bed and pull the covers over me.

I cry and cry. I hate religion. ◇

Moorings

Dale Walkonen

How old we become
catching fish by the sea,
gathering its plenty.

While, fathoms below,
shimmering pearls,
a fat mama shakes her hot hula;
swirling strength, she's unperturbed
by the play above of cloud and clear,
where winds gather force and waves take birth.

In quiet's tide pool, clocks tick our pulse,
chairs furnish our moorings.

We long for the bright flash
of new-found fish,
but heave heavy chests,
memory's tattered trousseau,
thick with barnacles,
weighed down by the draperies
that clothe our dreams.

Still, nothing is lost, or left behind.
It all travels with us,
waits for the wise old lady to shimmy and shake.

In each of us, a hot hula mama,
whose hips are hungry for ease,
for mating with the wild
unburdened ocean, dances
where fish find shelter,
where the eye,
turning with a twist of thought,
spins the stuff to iridescence,
swirling strength that holds our power. ◇

Mime Funeral
for Marcel Marceau, 1923-2007

Dale Walkonen

The bips assemble at sunset;
their eyes blaze with reflected light,
keep watch on the horizon,
as the vessel that once transported them,
is swallowed by the sea.

The first bip, father Bip,
no longer pressing against the wind,
surrenders to water and fire.

His last mask, the still and silent one,
passes into the night.
He exchanges his human face for a diamond.

What worlds will he explore, astronaut extraordinaire,
his art, an exquisite craft
re-fashioned
for traveling universes?

The bips, white-faced, pass among themselves
quiet gestures of remembrance,
knowing they too are facets of the jewel.
Inheritors of an ancient art,
they listen for cadences in the blood,
a marceau code,
that compresses space,
that possesses all of time.

The bips turn soft steps and take divergent roads
back to the places where people suffer and laugh.
Bip birds, ravens, seagulls, plovers,
return to all the villages of the world,

where hearts, longing to take wing,
feel the uplift
of a warm and tender wind:

as if they heard silence,
or the elegant passage of silence,
into eternity. ◇

Rose

Elisabeth von Uhl

Red plaid over her arm,
next to the stainless steel
cane and everyday it is tea
with two sugars and a different
doctor. I doubt she prays
to something that took her sister,
never gave her a child. Yet,
she wears gold want around
her neck—a cross stealing over
what used to be cleavage,
now bound so tight; she
clenches her fist like teeth
that once tore white flesh. ◇

3274 Hull Avenue

Elisabeth von Uhl

Yet the bud forces
itself through the ground

to be cut, scalded, and packed
into the rafters, under the foundation,

through the windows
of the house filled of flesh

and fur. We make love, we
make anger between these walls.

To us, our hunger
goes unnoticed and voices

thicken the air between doors,
within cupboards, and under floors.

Our hands rake the earth of itself.
We take breath. ◇

New Rochelle's Cynthia Ozick

An Interview

Debra Banerjee

Cynthia Ozick liberally sprinkles her conversation with quotes from Henry James, Shakespeare, Tolstoy—and Martin Luther *in German*. This fluency in the languages of literature comes as second nature to the esteemed novelist, short-story writer, and essayist, who describes herself as "bookish." Acclaimed for her cerebral, literary works, often on Jewish themes and moral issues, Ozick was the subject of a National Endowment for the Arts–sponsored documentary film on writers that made its debut during the 2009 Big Read program. Her novella *The Shawl*, published in 1989, was chosen for the community-wide cultural event. Ozick shared her thoughts on writing and writers during an interview with *The Westchester Review*, at her home in Westchester.

Born in 1928, Ozick was raised in the Pelham Bay section of the Bronx, not far from the historic district of New Rochelle, where she has lived since 1961. Her family has had roots in Westchester since 1912. Her latest novel, *Foreign Bodies*, completed shortly before this interview, will be published in 2011.

WR: What do you feel when you finish a book?
CO: Relief! What an albatross comes off your shoulders! I'm in that state now. If you think I'm sitting down, I'm actually levitating a little bit. It doesn't last long, then comes the anxiety. Suddenly that which was extremely isolated, very private, becomes public, and anything that becomes public becomes vulnerable. It's that kind of anxiety about reception.

WR: Are you anxious about the critical response?
CO: It's the critical response.

WR: Is there a sense of sadness, this creative piece is coming to an end?
CO: No, it's relinquished; I have nothing more to say. I've done everything I could do and had all the thoughts on these particular themes relevant to this particular book that I could possibly have. And, in fact, what I'm roiling with now is I want to do some short stories now as a kind of counterpoint to the long haul and this is what I am mulling day and night. I have a lot of ideas and I have to choose one, and then there's the worry: you don't want a short story to be an anecdote or anecdotal in any way. It's got to have some gravitas. I'm in the mulling process before sitting down and writing. When I get the first sentence, I'll be able to begin.

WR: How do you find working with editors?
CO: As far as I'm concerned, it [the work] is done. I am really obsessively meticulous, as every comma counts for me, and it's all been thought through, and my ideal copy editor—and I do have an ideal copy editor—is someone who doesn't touch a syllable. Except, I make mistakes in arithmetic, which leads me to terrible mistakes in chronology. I can give you two examples: at the end of *Heir to a Glimmering World*, I had lilacs blooming in autumn and they pointed out that this was not possible; but more than that, my London agent found something arithmetically absurd. He found that I had arranged for an eleven-month pregnancy, so that is what I need help with.

WR: So do your editors give you carte blanche to keep every comma in place?
CO: Oh, absolutely; I wouldn't stand for anything else. I do know how to spell, too. Some writers don't.

WR: Do you work on projects simultaneously?
CO: When there's a long project, it gets interrupted. The current novel was interrupted for some months because I was working on a novella. I got a couple of prizes and I had to write talks, which are basically long essays. Then I wrote another long essay for *Harper's*, because I also do nonfiction. Every time you return to it with this kind of interruption, it's ice-cold. And you have to get back in, worm your way back into that tunnel again.

WR: How do you do that?
CO: It's hard! You've been away and you've been working on something else and your mind-set is toward something else, and you come back and you look at the text and it seems foreign to you. What it takes is a kind of grit and force, and you say, "I will force my way in," and you do that. Once you've forced your way in, then you seem to find it, but it takes a push.

WR: It's gratifying to hear that a writer such as yourself struggles.
CO: Writing is hard.

WR: But for you, I'm sure, there's no other way of life.
CO: I always compare it to what Luther said in a different context, *"Ich kann nicht anders."* I can do no other. Without this, what? Writers are born. I can't remember who said this: "Writing is harder for writers than it is for other people." If you belong to a literate population, you write. Writing is part of life—the grocery list, if nothing more. But writers don't write like that. It's art. It is a kind of paradox that writing is harder for writers.

WR: How do you perceive your own gift?
CO: I don't know how to answer that.

WR: Do you see it as a gift?

CO: I know that it's a gift, but how one perceives it oneself? It is a gift; you're not responsible for it. It is an inborn thing, that's what a gift is, but there's really no sense of owning a gift. Henry James said it: "We work in the dark." That's what it feels like, so when you're working in the dark and you're looking for that glimmer of light, you're not thinking, "How fortunate I am; I have a gift." The whole idea of gift doesn't pertain. "We work in the dark—we do what we can—we give what we have." It's a very valuable quote. It's pinned up over my desk. "The rest is the madness of art."

It's much more related to the idea of madness rather than gift. It is after all a kind of madness. You sit alone, you're working in the dark. You're making things up that don't exist. You're creating conflict, drama, emotions, villains. You enter into the marrow and soul and bone of these bad people. It's a kind of demonic interchange. You kind of change your soul for the bad guy's soul. There's something monstrous about writers. Every work of fiction has something demonic about it or it wouldn't be worth writing. Writing is really a repetition of the book of Genesis. It's about sin, about the knowledge of sin, good and evil, deep-engrained early human myths.

WR: When did you know you wanted to be a writer?

CO: I knew from the age of five. Before I could write, my mother indulgently copied my poems. I remember two words of a poem that she seemed proud of as she copied it. It began "Oh, moon!" I also had an uncle who was a poet, so I knew that such a thing existed in the world and you could be that. Of course he was a starving poet with five children that he had trouble feeding. I didn't think about that side of it, just that it was something you could do.

WR: Did your parents encourage you?

CO: My mother in particular.

WR: Are there characters from your books that you identify with?

CO: They're all invented, but there are occasionally aspects with which I do identify. If there's a bookish character, that's the self.

WR: Do you do a lot of research for your books?
CO: No, that's why I like to write fiction. I don't have to do all that work. That's another reason to write fiction—laziness.

WR: One gets a sense from reading your books that you know so much about the world. Where does your worldliness come from?
CO: I don't feel worldly. I often define myself as unworldly. I think it's mostly from books, and worldliness is from getting knocked about in the outer world. Between the two of us, *you* have to be the worldly one. Mine is mostly bookishness. I wouldn't call that worldly. I would call it a kind of interiority.

History, that's an even playing field, because none of us have lived in the past. We can all be equally worldly about history.

WR: Do you read constantly?
CO: Constantly. I read everything. We get a tremendous number of periodicals, that's aside from books. What I'm reading now is A. S. Byatt's *The Children's Book*. It's so enchanting. Reading this, I have the feeling of being a child again and reading like that, as a child, which is one of those rapturous things you remember. Reading as an adult has never been like that.

WR: What writers do you admire?
CO: I've always been enthralled by Bellow, and Updike and Alice Munro, and I also read history.

WR: How do story ideas come to you?
CO: Different writers have different answers. I used to talk about this with a friend who's a writer. She said it was psychological and emotional. I said that it came from an idea. That sounds dry and abstract. There's a seamlessness between idea and emotion, that emotions are ideas and ideas are emotions. We were saying the same thing, but coming from different passages. Then there's that famous Tolstoyan comment, "If you

see that brawl in the street or doorway you can write *War and Peace*." You can write about big wars, and there's something to that. It's like saying, "Where does imagination come from?" It's a mysterious thing and we really don't know. It's like, "What is a dream?" It's a mystery.

WR: What is your writing process?
CO: Middle of the night. I start very late.

WR: Do you sit down every day to write?
CO: I try to sit down every day to work. Sometimes the exigencies of life prevent you. I work within the normal span of human energy. But I do go on deep into the night, because of the quiet. You kind of own the world.

WR: Is your husband asleep?
CO: I've corrupted him. He stays up now, but we're in different rooms. We have a long corridor between our desks.

WR: Do you sleep late?
CO: Oh, God, yes!

WR: Do you work on a computer?
CO: No, I work on a desk, with a felt-tip pen, on sheets that I get at Staples, that are very finely lined, in very tiny handwriting. When I first had the computer, I had an interim stage. I would use the typewriter because my handwriting became illegible and it's tiny and it's all mushed together, so I would type it then and do little fiddlings on the typewriter, then go to the computer for good copy and fiddle with it some more. Then I couldn't get typewriter ribbons. So I had to give up the interim typewriter. Now I go directly to the computer and fiddle with the computer.

My worksheets for the finished book are really towering, lots and lots of fiddling. I just put them in a box and put them in the cellar.

WR: Do you do a draft?

CO: No drafts. I am not a draft writer. I can't conceive of it. You might say each sentence is a draft. I won't let go of that sentence until I perfect it. I may be slovenly in every other way, but not with sentences. I can't conceive of writers who can bear to leave slapdash, unformed stuff on the page and say, "I'll finish it later." How can you behave like that? Would you wash a kitchen floor like that—splash—and then say, "I'll come back and finish it later"?

WR: So each sentence is crafted, it doesn't just flow?
CO: Each sentence is crafted absolutely. Some sentences you're lucky and it comes to you.

WR: Do you know the whole story in your mind from start to finish?
CO: Mostly no. It begins in chaos and the chaos lasts for a long time. When you get to something like the three-quarters point, things begin to dovetail and rush away, and it gets very, very exciting, and that's really the best part, toward the end. E. L. Doctorow said something very useful about writing: "It's like driving a car at night. You never see further than your headlights, but you can make the whole trip that way." I think that's a very good description. Philip Roth also said something interesting: "Writing is problem-solving." I think that's a helpful description.

WR: One critic called your characters irritating.
CO: Have you ever read the reader responses on Amazon? It's interesting to see what readers want. They don't want downbeat, they don't want characters who aren't lovable. Then I say, "How can you bear King Lear or Iago?" Don't you want writing to be like life? You want to love your characters. As a reader I, too, want to love my characters, but I'm not sure Shakespeare is going to allow me to love his characters. And sometimes an unlovable character can be a great character.

WR: Speaking of irritating characters, there's Rosa in *The Shawl*. How did the story of *The Shawl* come to you?

CO: That is an interesting thing. In theory, I don't think we can make fiction out of this [the Holocaust] because we weren't there. Something happened to me one day; I've never had that experience before and never had after, and it's something I always denied; I don't believe in it. But it did happen for some reason. I had this sense in the first section that a voice was dictating to me. That's a grandiose thing to say, but that's how I felt. I'm never fluent, and I was fluent in that section. The second part, called "Rosa," was writing, like any other writing. That was normal. But the early part, the part that takes place in the camp, which I never was in, that I don't think anybody had a right to imagine because it's a kind of subversion of the people who were there. But that's what happened, and that's how I came to write it in a mysterious way that I can't account for and don't even believe in, but that's the truth.

WR: How would you like to be remembered?
CO: The assumption behind that is that one will be remembered. That is not a reliable assumption. I can think of so many writers who, the minute they disappeared from the world of the living, an eclipse occurred. Updike is permanent. And how do we know that in advance? It's time that makes that judgment. All levels of readers have said about Updike, "I thought he would never go away. I thought he would always be there." I hear that again and again. I think that's a pretty good guarantee. Very few writers would leave you with that feeling of such a dreadful loss. Most writers, once they're absent physically, then they become absent as writers. I don't expect to be remembered. It wouldn't stop me from writing because what else am I going to do? I have thought about this and I'm pretty sure.

Now there's a downbeat ending. How irritating! ◇

Three Visits

Jessica Bennett

I.

My mother sits on the couch
where she has been for years.
Outside the window behind her

tall stalks of joe-pye weed sway in the wind.
She tells me about my father,
handsome, not that looks matter,

how she dismissed him
as dull the day they met.
Unimpressive, really—

In uniform, walking up a dusty road
till he wiped the grime off his wire rims.
She's in the 1940s, and oh, how she loves him—

and the faintly purple flowers swing
to and fro in the frame
behind her diminished head as if

they work for her, back-up singers
humming along as she waxes on about their bond,
till death do us part,

for the wonderful hardships
of the war. *We needed nothing—*
And the weeds wave, bob and sway

*—but each other—*and windows begin
to sing in the wind. My mother slows,
losing threads of her

story, eyes watery with something
important, something
forgotten.

I ask a question
to wind her up again
but she's startled

by this intermission
of the present, of being alone.
She asks *when?*

whenever did I happen
to come in, and how long
was my drive?

II.

Wrapped in blue today, she wakes to watch
the wide pigeon-colored sky and the

traffic at the feeder. She naps here and there
until a band of jays comes to feed.

This is how she passes time. Her twisted hands
can no longer hold her book, her drink,

her trademark cigarette—Even words come
tangled, or like today, not at all.

A chipmunk sits on the windowsill stuffing
his cheeks with oily seeds. She's always admired

diligence in preparing for a hungry season.
She reaches out and pulls the pile of daily

papers scattered on the couch onto her lap
as if a blanket of printed words will keep her safe.

III.

The hayfields are golden this afternoon.
My mother wants to go somewhere—she cannot say
where—but she takes my hand
to feel the sun and breeze of an open window.

Together, we watch a gathering flock of starlings
settle in the trees. Another flock merges and settles.
Soon all the maples are alive with iridescent
blackbirds shifting, flapping and chattering.

Thousands upon thousands of birds make the trees look dark.
The beating of wings takes over and they lift off
all at once and fly over the house. They rise up
like a black silk scarf carried away by wind.

Birds shift and turn back over us,
their wheeling makes the ground undulate, swell
and shrink beneath us. We are dizzy with movement
though we are standing still.

It is as if we are on the bow of a boat, she says.

In this moment, I am ready to let her go. ◇

Weekend Gardener

Lesleigh Forsyth

The earth grows rocks, I've heard,
snow-crumble fertilized, then birthed up
into bassinet spring. Will she give back
the ring she borrowed from my pinky,
six-years-long, occupied with bubble soap,
the way my mother (no more her girl-self,
but playing curl and petticoat)
borrowed me to wear it? Or perhaps
she kept the golden angel-topper herself,
root bound, moss-wed to a stepping stone.

How she neglects this plot, showing
off her cliffs, ravines; never prunes
my thorn-sewn circle path.
Did she return it by mistake to some
placid weeder, star-slipped into a future
of finding, instead of to this persistent
treasure seeker, who still twirls
dirt between hyacinths and green bells,
shear-searches vines up into the holly,
persists in loss, even of the found? ◇

Questions for Bruce Hungerford

Lesleigh Forsyth

You must have walked this way along the sound
one street past your house,
strict clean cube that taunts the Victorian parade,
seen grosgrain ribbons of sun on water,
dry stalks of marsh grass whiten,
angle into egrets' necks.

Did you learn slow scales watching gulls
pad across striations in Manhattan schist?
Arpeggios from a heron's loop through swashy reeds?
Were there answers in the intermittent
counterpoint of wind and ripple?
Did they vanish in the lift of shore birds
out of their sculpted silhouettes?

I've seen the photo you took at Abu Simbel,
timed, timeless—self of self at temple's base,
　　your pedal foot perpendicular to Ramses'
　　your body the size of his wrist
　　your hand raised in performance
　　at the practice keyboard on spindle legs.
Was it Beethoven you played on silent keys?
What did you hear in that silence
massive as the chiseling it took
to dam the Nile? ◇

Hungerford was a distinguished concert pianist who lived in Larchmont, N.Y. He was also an amateur photographer and Egyptologist. The photograph mentioned in the poem was a timed exposure he took of himself on a trip to Abu Simbel. At the time, he was preparing to record the complete Beethoven sonatas, a project that was not completed due to his tragic death in a road accident at the age of fifty-four.

Pan Tadeusz

Thaddeus Rutkowski

I N THE MORNING, MY FATHER DROVE ME TO SCHOOL BECAUSE I HAD missed the bus. I'd missed it because my father was talking to me.

"I don't care if you go to school," he said as he steered his car. "I don't want you to associate with American kids. When I was in school, I had no friends. That's why they called me 'The Brain.'"

"I say, to hell with this educational system," he continued. "You're going to learn what Polish schoolchildren know. You're going to read Adam Mickiewicz's epic poem, *Pan Tadeusz*. You'll start by memorizing a hundred lines. Then you'll recite to me."

As we rode, cold air blew through the seams of the car's flimsy convertible roof. Mornings brought a chill in this part of Appalachia.

"Do you know who Mickiewicz was? Mickey was a poet and a hero! There are statues of Mickey all over Poland!"

I looked at the gas gauge. The needle sat almost at Empty. "Is it time to get gas?" I asked.

"Don't interrupt me!" my father replied. "You're going to learn about the lost country of Lithuania and the noble families who lived there. If you don't pick up anything else, you'll have better manners."

WHEN I TOLD MY MOTHER about my father's assignment, she said, "That's the Polish way. I know nothing about it. I know my own way, the Chinese way. But if you want to be part of this family, you've got to act like a Pole."

"How about you?" I asked. "Did you convert?"

"I learned to cook like a Pole—from my mother-in-law. After I met your father in college here, that was a condition of marrying into his family."

I STARTED TO READ *PAN TADEUSZ*. The poem was in a small book with a plain-red hard cover.

I couldn't understand why a traveler named Thaddeus arrived at a farm, caught a glimpse of a swan-necked woman next to a pond, and shared a meal with the people of the estate. These people spent a lot of time hunting hares and loading sheaves of rye.

I put the book down, pulled on my clodhoppers, and went to visit an Amish friend. I rode my bike a few miles, then crossed a field on foot. In the open, a bull spotted me and started to charge. The animal bellowed as it came. Its horns had been cut off, but the loss seemed to have aggravated its anger. When it got closer, it began to dig at the ground with a front hoof. Clouds of moisture sprayed from its nostrils.

I hopped a fence and reached the farmhouse. I knocked on a side door while looking into the dark interior. I saw a dog sleeping on an upholstered chair, and a woman with a headscarf sitting next to a cast-iron stove.

My friend came to the door.

"I'd like to walk to your pond," I said.

"I'll go with you," he said.

The two of us hiked across fields until we came to a crater filled with water.

"The pond almost went dry," my friend said, "but your father brought a drainpipe to fix it."

I looked into the water and saw a thick iron cylinder standing on end. Water was flowing into the mouth of the pipe and leaving from under the pond's embankment.

"We jammed the pipe into the ground," my friend said, "and the water rose, but most of the fish died."

I could see the Amish family's barn in the distance. It looked sturdy and newly painted. "Your building is in great shape," I said.

"Someone burned our old barn down," my friend said.

"Who did it?"

"It happened while we were asleep. We saw a truck driving away, but we couldn't see its license plate. Ours was the fourth barn burned in this valley."

"Why did they do it?"

"They like to see things burn."

On our way back from the pond, my friend brought me to a chicken shed. "Have you ever seen a green egg?" he asked.

He unlatched a rickety door and led me inside. I saw a bird-shaped object on the floor. It was on its back, with its curled wings pointing upward. "Is that a dead chicken?" I asked.

"Yes."

"Why is it on the floor?"

"No one has taken it out yet."

I looked around the small, hot room for green eggs.

"You know," my friend said, "sometimes I think about leaving the faith. I'd like to have a truck instead of a horse, and maybe a telephone. I'd like to smoke tobacco."

THAT NIGHT, I noticed that my mother didn't offer Polish food. Instead, she served a mixture of rice and Chinese cabbage. My brother and sister and I used American utensils. My father wasn't present; I guessed he was at the local bar.

I picked up a pair of chopsticks; I'd learned from my mother how to hold them. But my brother and sister didn't follow my lead.

THE NEXT TIME MY FATHER AND I WERE IN HIS CAR, he tested my knowledge of *Pan Tadeusz*.

"What does the title mean?" he asked.

"Sir Thaddeus," I said.

"That's right. Now, recite!"

I was silent.

My father pressed the accelerator, and air began to whistle around the edges of the car's vinyl roof.

"I see you'd rather horse around than listen to the old man."

"I went to see a friend," I said.

"I'm the judge," my father said. "You're a peasant. In the poem, the judge decides what happens with peasants."

The car's engine banged a couple of times, then went dead. "We're out of gas," my father said.

I waited while my father walked to a fueling station. His trip took a long time. When he came back, he was carrying a large can with a goose-necked spout.

He removed the gas cap on the rear fender and funneled liquid into the opening. When he turned the key, the engine churned but wouldn't catch. He repeated the steps without success.

Presently, a passing motorist stopped and said, "You need to prime the carburetor."

My father lifted the hood, unfastened a metal lid, and poured a small amount of gasoline down the engine's throat. When he turned the key again, we heard a small explosion. Then we heard the cylinders engage. In a moment, the engine was spinning like a top.

On the way home, my father stopped at a roadside bar. I sat at a Formica-topped table with him. He had a bourbon and a beer, while I had a ginger ale. "You will go to your room," he said, "and you will not come out until you've memorized a hundred lines."

IN MY ROOM, I ignored the Polish epic. I lit a stick of incense and let it smolder. Then I lit a hand-rolled tobacco cigarette and smoked it. I looked out my window and imagined there was another country on the other side of the nearest mountain. I could climb over the ridge to get to the other realm. Boulders strewn along the summit wouldn't stop me. On top, I would look over and see a city. I'd walk down the other side and come to a street. The street would take me to a customs office. I'd show my identity papers and cross.

I opened *Pan Tadeusz*. Sir Thaddeus was leaving the farm. He was saying goodbye to the swan-necked woman. His head and the woman's head touched like the tops of two trees in a storm.

I shut my eyes and mouthed the words. I thought it wouldn't take long to commit a hundred lines to memory. ◇

Mami

Marlena Maduro Baraf

I CAN ALMOST TOUCH THE MEMORY OF MY MOTHER ON THAT DAY IN the patio under the calabash tree. I must have been in the kitchen when I heard my *tío* Neto's voice, quiet but firm. I stepped out and I saw her. I see her *cuerpo*, her animal body, her flesh, dense and still, like wax. Her eyes don't see me, they are unfocused. Her beautiful bearing has sunk into itself. I cannot tell if she is listening to my uncle. I don't remember anything I might have said. I was seven. We can see so much when we are seven. We can see everything. Our pupils are like open coconut holes sucking in the images; our ears almost hurt, the cells expand to near bursting to reach a point of understanding.

Not even today, many years after her death, does anyone really know what was wrong with my mother. In the fifties and sixties the treatment was electric shock therapy and a staple of asylum medicine, Thorazine.

For me, for my older sister, and for our baby brother, she was our mother, inescapably our *mamá*. She was a piece of us like a nose or budding breasts. When she pressed the fleshy part of her thumb against her molars, again and again, we were her thumb. We could not unplug from her actions. We begged her to stop. She couldn't. She would turn her head back to talk to us her anxiety when driving us places, making us crazy afraid of total annihilation in the streets of Panama. She caressed her breasts by reaching down into the round scoop of her tropical dresses, as if to comfort herself. We, prepubescent daughters, were mortified by her lack of self-censorship, as when she walked in clammy nakedness in her bedroom, unaffected by us.

When *Mami* came to our school, she begged the nuns to pray for her. We were not Catholic, but *Mami* desperately sought help from anyone who might have special access. She greedily developed any illness that struck a friend or a relative, relished feeling the pain, and demanding the medication.

"Están gordas." "You are fat," she would insist. "What is wrong with you? Why doesn't anyone like you?" The torrent of hurts drove my sister out of the house or into the retreat of depression. I was naturally sunny; I was a watcher, capable of playing the game. Needing desperately a mother. I analyzed and studied and understood. *Mami* was sick. "They hate me. *Me odian. Me quieren matar,"* she told anyone who would listen. As was typical when she took to her bed in a self-induced illness, I became the emissary between her and "the evil maids." I had the job of bringing meals to her on the white tray with the hinged sides, the hot milk in the Mikasa cup, and the English silver setting.

I place the tray down on the bed and she begins her recitation. "They want to poison me! They have poisoned the food."

"Mami, it is not poisoned," I tell her. "I promise you, *te juro, te lo juro,* there is no poison. I saw the preparation with my own eyes."

The moment always arrives, *"Entonces pruébalo."* "Taste it then."

Good little girl that I am, I taste the bitter truth. With every swallow, I bury a piece of myself. I do remember now the lack of me, an oppressive nonbeing. Wiped out. ◇

Brother's Keeper

Kathleen Williamson

THUMP. AGAIN, THUMP.

I open one eye and see it's getting light out, but the light looks funny, gray or something. *Thump.* I sit up and pull back my shade and a blizzard is raging. There must be a foot of snow on the ground.

Thump. I get up. "Mom?" I pass my parents' room. It's a Saturday morning but their bed's already made. I stop at the door to Devin's room. *Thump.* I crack it open and I see my brother sitting on his bed, banging his head against the wall.

"Hey, Buddy? What ya doin'?" I hate the sound of my voice. You know, that forced good cheer you use when you're talking to a baby or a puppy? But Devin's not a baby or a puppy and certainly not my buddy. He's more like an alien dropped into my world to make me miserable. *Thump.*

"Mom? Dad?" I run down the stairs lined with what must be a hundred photos of me and Devin from the time of his christening to his graduation from middle school last year. There's no milestone my mother finds too insignificant to memorialize with a studio portrait. Every photo's posed the same: I've got a chubby arm around my little brother and I'm wearing a big fake smile and my teeth stick out more each year. No big shock that the kids call me Alvin—as in "and the Chipmunks." Devin's smiling, too, but he's never looking at the camera.

Thump. I run to the kitchen and throw the light switch but the fluorescent bulb doesn't blink on. No car in the driveway. Of course. My parents are stuck on Long Island in this stupid storm. I pick up the phone but there's no dial tone—no electricity, no phone, duh.

Thump. I run back upstairs to Devin in his room. Unlike the rest of our house, which is littered with files and books and baseball caps and sneakers, Devin's room is empty. I'm not talking neat, I'm talking empty. Not a toy, not a picture on the wall. The therapists said that Devin shouldn't get overstimulated. So everything was removed, even the cross that used to hang above his bed. The room's only got his bed, his bureau, and a single mirror tacked onto the wall at floor level. The therapists use the mirror for working on eye contact. Devin's got major issues with looking you in the eye. His room gives me the creeps and I hardly ever go in there. Today it smells like wet diapers and I see he's peed in his bed.

"Jeez Louise, Devin. What happened here?"

Devin's crying hard now but at least he's stopped banging his head.

"Where's Mommy?" he asks in that eerie robotic voice of his. "Mommy brings me to the bathroom every morning at seven o'clock a.m. She says, 'Good morning, sunshine' and brings me to the bathroom every morning at seven o'clock a.m.."

I look at the clock: Seven twenty. Devin wouldn't change routine even to take a piss. Man, why did Mom and Dad have to go to that wedding?

I feel guilty for even thinking that. My parents never go anywhere and they really like Anna, the girl who got married. She's been working with Devin longer than any of his other therapists—like seven years or something. My mom hadn't wanted to go but my dad said, "Goddamn it, Pauline, Timothy's fifteen years old, he's perfectly capable of putting Devin to bed for one night." Miraculously, my dad won that argument.

So we'd prepared—for weeks. I generally don't have much to do with Devin, but we practiced a lot for the big day. And, you know, it really went okay. Devin said, "Timothy is putting Devin to bed tonight—just this once!" about a hundred million times. It was kind of annoying but kind of nice, too. I'd never been too sure that Devin even *knew* my name before. What we hadn't prepared for was a surprise snowstorm in early December and a blackout on top of that. Shit.

Now you're probably thinking that I should run next door to a neighbor's house or something, but that's because you don't know us Fitzgeralds. It's not like we've had much time for socializing, with Devin and all. When he's not running away, he's shrieking or grabbing at his penis or something. And then there's my dad; he's like an open wound. Someone will ask a question about Devin, which they're bound to do since he's so weird, and my dad acts like they're sticking their finger into his gut and wiggling it around. I hear the kids in the neighborhood call him Mr. Fisticuffs under their breath. My dad would kill me if he found out I was knocking on Mr. Rizzo's door or rapping at Mrs. Stolinowski's front window. Nope, we Fitzgeralds stick to ourselves.

So I'm just standing there next to Devin's bed listening to him cry and screech. To tell you the truth, I'd just as soon leave him lying there in his own piss but then I think of my mom and I figure there's no way I could ever look her in the eye again if I did that. My mom's a saint. I know, I know, people say that crap all the time, but I think it's literally true about my mom. She says, "Timothy, Devin's *in* there, and all we have to do is find the key." And man, oh, man, she will not give up. And she doesn't care how much the "cure" costs. She doesn't buy herself a goddamn thing—except those stupid studio portraits. She works double shifts at Mother Cabrini Hospital and when she's home she's busy coordinating therapists' schedules.

There's nothing she won't try: Floor-time, Applied Behavior Analysis, music therapy, Son-Rise program, gluten/casein–free diet. The *cure du jour* is something called a hyperbaric chamber, where Devin gets into this pressurized, oxygen-filled tube. It's been used for treating the bends that scuba divers can get. Some snake-oil salesman came up with the idea of using it to cure autism. To tell you the truth, I don't buy into any of it. I don't think there's anything that'll cure Devin and my mom's just wasting her time—just like my grandmother, who wore out her knees praying the Rosary and begging for our relief.

I'm racking my brain trying to get Devin to stop screeching. And then I have one of those light-bulb moments and I say, "Hey, Buddy, you wanna go to Grand Central?" Devin stops shrieking. I'm pretty proud of myself for coming up with the idea, until I take another look out the window. Fuck it. Too late now, we've got to go.

"We'll see Thomas the Tank Engine?" Devin asks.

"Of course, Buddy, we'll see Thomas."

There's a Thomas exhibit at the little transit museum in Grand Central. In case you don't know, Thomas the Tank Engine is an animated television show about all these different train engines. Each engine's got a different face and personality and they have all these little problems that get worked out by the end of the show. It's pretty idiotic if you want to know the truth. The show's made for preschoolers but it's got this hold on autistic kids. Anna says it's because of the rigidity of having to stay on the tracks, but I don't know.

Once Devin makes up his mind he moves fast. His wet pajamas are on the floor and he rummages through his drawer and pulls out Thomas the Tank Engine underwear and T-shirt. The T-shirt is skintight and the elastic on his underpants digs into his thighs; they don't make that shit to fit thirteen-year-olds, but I don't care, at least he's not crying anymore. I get dressed, too. We eat a couple of frozen Pop-Tarts (so much for his gluten/casein–free diet) and I help Devin with his boots and mittens and we're out of the house by seven forty-five.

The wind's howling and it whips Devin's Thomas the Tank Engine hat right off his head and over Mr. Rizzo's seven-foot fence. Devin's blubbering again so I take off my hat and pull it down over his ears. "Here, crybaby, let's get to the train."

We only live about four blocks from the Dobbs Ferry train station but it's tough going. No one's shoveled yet and the snow's up to our knees. I pull Devin over a snow bank and into the street just as a plow rumbles past, spewing rock salt all over us. Then the asshole driver leans on his horn and we both jump about four feet. It's so cold, my ears are stinging and then, wham, I get a snowball to the back of the head followed by a "Hey, Aaalviin!" Goddamn Robby Wolfe. Doesn't the kid have a home? The whole way to the station I've got one hand around Devin's wrist and I'm shaking the snow out of my shirt with the other.

When we get to the platform we make our way to the timetable. The thing must be three feet by five feet and every train line known to mankind is on it and I can't make heads or tails of it. Devin looks at it for about two seconds and announces, "The next train from Dobbs Ferry to Grand Central Terminal is at eight twenty a.m. The next train is at nine twenty a.m. Then the next train is at nine fifty-six a.m. Then the next train is at ten twenty a.m." Man, the kid's a mystery. Other kids call him a retard but I don't know anybody else on the planet who can figure out a schedule as fast as he can. And now he'll know it by heart for the rest of his godforsaken life.

That's the good news. The bad news is the train is late. And, man, oh, man, Devin does not "do" late. He's jumping up and down grabbing at himself through his jacket and the wind is so cold I bet his tears are turning to ice on his cheeks. And there's not a thing I can do, because I know he won't listen to *me*. At least the platform's empty so he's not putting on a show for anyone.

When the train finally comes, we make our way down to the last car and Devin stands by the back window, rocking and repeating, "Thomas, Percy, Gordon." Those are his favorite engines in Thomas the Tank Engine. We're warming up and feeling pretty good when the door between the cars slides open.

"Tickets, please," the conductor slurs.

Shit. I left my cash on the kitchen table. I check all my pockets and then start patting down Devin, but I come up with maybe two dollars.

I start explaining my lack of cash to the conductor but he's not interested. I can smell the liquor on his breath, and his face under his flat-topped cap is the color of raw liver.

"That's it, boy. No money, no ticket, no ride. You're off at the next station."

I look out the window. The snow's falling sideways now, and I'm like, "You've got to be fucking kidding me."

He grabs me by the collar and Devin starts shrieking. The train's practically empty and the few passengers on it don't even look up. They just turn up the volume on their iPods. The train starts to slow down for the next station and I'm thinking of taking a swing at the guy, when the door between the cars slides open again and another, younger conductor comes in.

He comes right up to us and says, "Joe, what the hell is going on?"

Joe looks around a little bleary-eyed and lets me go. "Sean, the kid's got no ticket, no money, and a fresh mouth."

Sean places his hand on Joe's arm. I can tell he knows Joe's a drunk. "Look at these poor kids." He indicates Devin with a tilt of his chin. "My nephew's like this poor creature here." He shakes his head. "Joe, look at the snow."

Joe mutters something but ends up shrugging and walking away. Sean turns to me now and says, "Kid, when you get into Grand Central, give someone a call or something, okay? Take care of your brother here."

I'm still shaking but I'm with it enough to see there's a little puddle on the streaked linoleum: Devin's wet himself.

In Grand Central we have to cross the Main Concourse to get to the Transit Museum. I've never seen it so empty. There are only a handful of people and most of them are either cops or National Guardsmen. They've been stationed here since 9/11 and they're always standing around in full jungle camouflage. I gotta laugh. They'd be better off wearing something that makes them look like they're blending in with the marble columns or something.

We come here a lot. Other families go to the movies or to ball games; the Fitzgeralds go Grand Central, mostly because of Devin's obsession with trains, but I love it here, too. If you've never been, you really ought to go—it puts St. Pat's to shame. The ceiling rises a hundred and twenty-five feet—I know that for a fact. And there's constellations painted on it in gold, with stars actually twinkling. Not everyone knows this, but the constellations are painted backwards. The Vanderbilts, the dudes that built the terminal, told everyone that's because the ceiling reflected God's view of the heavens, but I think the painter just made a mistake.

The ceiling itself is this great blue-teal color—the same shade as a catbird's egg. I know that because we once had a catbird build a nest in a prickly bush right outside our kitchen window and it laid a perfect little egg. My parents and I waited for it to hatch for weeks. Then one day we saw it had cracked open, but instead of a baby bird, all that was there was a runny, drippy mess.

I've got Devin by the wrist again and we're making our way slowly past the four-sided clock at the information desk when, bam! the sun comes out and light streams in every window, in great shafts. It's awesome. It reminds me of God. Not that I believe in God. Not anymore.

My dad stopped believing right after Devin's diagnosis. He said, "Why would God give you something so perfect and then take it away again?"

Then Father Donovan said something like, "Sure, now, isn't Devin a little gift from God?"

My dad never entered Our Lady of Lourdes again. I'm surprised he didn't punch Father Donovan's lights out, because my dad's not known for using restraint. He swung at his boss once and he hasn't worked since. My dad's not even welcome at his regular barstool at Doyle's. He doesn't do much of anything now. Just kind of sits around and greets the stream of therapists at our front door and shows them to Devin's room.

Devin's spinning in the shafts of light now, trying to catch the beams in his hand. One of the all-time benefits of being in the city with Devin is that nobody pays any attention to him. You have to be a lot wackier than Devin to get a rise out of anyone here. I'm kind of enjoying watching Devin have so much fun, but then the sun disappears as fast as it came out and I grab him by the wrist and continue on our way to the museum.

It's not open yet so we wait outside and Devin's back to rocking and chanting the Thomas-and-Percy-and-Gordon mantra. And miraculously, at ten sharp, a woman comes to the door and unlocks it. The whole process takes a long time because she's got these three-inch nails and it is not easy to do anything with three-inch nails. The

Thomas the Tank Engine exhibit is still up, thank God, and Devin's humming and rocking and wiggling his fingers at the outer edge of his right eye, like in a trance, you know? But every fifteen minutes or so he sort of looks in my direction and says, "Timothy brought Devin to see Thomas and Percy and Gordon."

We're there for a couple of hours and there's not another visitor. The fingernail lady keeps letting out these exasperated sighs and her nostrils keep twitching because Devin smells like piss, until she finally says, "That's it. Everybody out. It's time for my lunch."

"What? This museum doesn't close for lunch," I say.

"Well, today it does," she says. "No way am I working all day all alone just because Jeannette never made it here in this storm. I am not sitting here another minute listening to my stomach rumble and that boy ramble. No, sir, not another minute."

I'm kind of at a loss on what to do. My mother always talks about advocating for Devin, but the only thing I can think of doing is taking a swing at the fingernail lady and she must have fifty pounds on me.

So I say, "Come on, Buddy. We'll see some train engines up close," and I manage to steer Devin out of there without him losing it. Fingernail lady makes some satisfied noises deep in her throat and locks up behind us.

We're making our way across the concourse again when all of a sudden "Silver Bells" erupts from the loudspeakers and thousands of tiny lights start dancing on the ceiling. The lights start shimmying down and we're caught inside a simulated snowstorm. The flakes merge into tiny silver bells and I'm humming along, "It's Christmas time in the city . . ." when the lights morph into the jolliest crowd of shoppers you've ever seen: all bundled up, loaded down with presents wrapped and ready, jostling their way round and round the concourse. It's like being stuck in a giant kaleidoscope.

I turn to see what Devin thinks of the show and he's gone. Jeez fucking Louise. I look all over the concourse, but I don't see him anywhere. Sweat breaks out on my scalp and my stomach seizes. He's gone. Oh, my God, he's finally disappeared.

Oh, Jesus. Oh, God. Before, when I said I didn't believe in God anymore? Well, that's not exactly true because I pray, I pray a lot. I've been praying ever since my mom told me her plan to put Devin in a hyperbaric chamber. She was so sure that this would cure him. She *knew* it this time. It's three hundred dollars a pop and God knows how many times Devin would go into the chamber before my mom would give up on *that* miracle. And that money had been set aside for my orthodontics. My mom was cool, she really was. She said the decision was up to me. So I said, "Okay, Mom, if that's what you want," because I really love my mom. But the thing is, I really, really hate my teeth. They've started to stick out so much I can't close my lips all the way and I sort of breathe through my mouth. So I've been praying. Not for a cure or anything. I'm no fool. But for Devin to disappear. Not die—no body, no ugly funeral—just for him to be gone. Holy Mary, Mother of God, pray for us sinners.

I start running up and down the hallways, shouting Devin's name, but he's nowhere. I see a National Guardsman and I kind of walk up slowly to him; he looks pretty intimidating with his rifle and stuff. I push back my tears with the heel of my hand and say, "My little brother? He's autistic. And I guess he ran when the music and the lights started up," and I point to the show going on. "He's gone." The last two words came out with a sob and a spray of mucus. The guard is looking me up and down, when I see, off in the distance, a tiny figure running across the middle of one of the sixty-foot arched windows that line the east side of the concourse. I know it's Devin and he looks like he's *inside* the window.

I just stand there and point and the guardsman follows my finger and he, too, sees Devin. "How the hell did he get up there?" he asks me but all I can do is shrug. Devin's running back and forth and he looks like he's in midair. I've never seen anything like it. Did he sprout wings or something? The guard is talking into his miniature walkie-talkie on his shoulder and then takes off running and I follow. We run past the Oyster Bar and down the hall and there's an elevator I'd never noticed before. We take the elevator up and start following signs to the Campbell Apartment and we run down a corridor and then *we're* inside the window. We're running on a frosted glass catwalk and there are giant plates of glass on either side of us—if you look to the left you're looking at Lexington Avenue and to the right you're looking down at the concourse. And straight in front of us, about fifty feet or so, is Devin, running back and forth, his hands over his ears. And between him and us is a cop with a gun pointed straight at him.

I start screaming, "No!" and I head straight for the cop. He turns and points the gun at me and I see right away it's a taser. I drop to my knees and put my hands behind my head. I saw a kid get tasered on YouTube or at least I heard it. I couldn't even look at the computer screen, the begging and the screaming were so awful. I squeeze my eyes shut and I brace myself, but nothing happens. I peek out and see Devin standing over me, with the cop and the guardsman looming over his shoulder. But they've both got their mouths open in confusion and they don't look like they're going to shoot us anymore.

The cop pulls me to my feet and says, "How did he get up here?"

"I don't know, but he's kind of a genius about trains and stuff," I say.

The cop and the guardsman talk for a while and then the cop says we should wait with him until our parents can be contacted.

I tell the cop the whole sad story about the wedding and the electricity and Thomas the Tank Engine and he turns out to be a good guy and he tells me I did a good job, under the circumstances.

So Devin and I just wait there with him, suspended in midair. Then the sun comes out again and we're bathed in one of those great shafts of light. Devin looks me *straight in the eye*, and says, "Timothy and Devin share the same shadow," and he points to our shadow on the frosted catwalk. I'm so happy, I'm ready to hug him, but then Devin's back inside himself, rocking and humming. I guess my mom is right. Devin's *in* there, and I just got a peek inside the keyhole. ◇

Portrait of a Child on Her Fifth Birthday

Missy Egan Wey

Shafts of autumn sunlight
illuminate her face
matted on velvet,
in a frame brushed by gold.
Wheat-colored hair, drawn
smooth across her forehead,
encircles her ears,
brushes the nape of her slender neck.
Her gray eyes look away,
smudged sockets,
thumbprints of ash.

I remember the white smocked dress,
blue stitching, drawn snug
across my chest, high collar
fastened by a pin made of pearls;
starched puffed sleeves
that hid my shoulders,
bruised by the boy next door;
the stench of sawdust on his hands.
Coils of insulation muffle screams
of a child, left behind,
in a deserted attic. ◇

Slipping Away

Natalie Safir

Letting the cord drop from your hands,
the kite string you clutch sail up out of sight,
unlatching the cage that holds the crimson bird;

Praising the sun as it slips down a slot in the hill,
watching your shiny boat of dreams round
a faraway curve; waving adieu to the fires;

Allowing the sand, the years, the voices
to wash down your legs until only
echoes rebound from empty rocks;

Releasing the starred night, an infant's smile,
the house that felt like home, that first
bite of melon, desire's electric dance;

Holding the urn of ashes where the cat used to lie,
the photograph that once was your mother,
a lover's voice on a tape you cannot find;

Learning to see what is left ◇

The Regular

Joanna Valente

He was eating. The waitress poured coffee
into his cup, tenderly falling homeward
    some streaming onto the saucer, ringing around.

There were coffee rings on the end table in his
    mother's house. His father didn't give a damn about
furniture, not when it couldn't scream from beneath

    the weight of all the books. Moscow
was just like North Carolina, all of it furniture
    furniture from your aunt and uncle, furniture

        waiting outside on the curb
to be picked up by women, not girls. Fritz, is this
    going to be it? the waitress asked like he was

    her father (who moved out with a
young girl almost her age). He was surprised
that Fritz was still his name, it hadn't changed

    like his body shrinking (could it one day
    be gone? like the snowman he made at eight
before they moved). No, that will be it, he said, indefinitely. ◇

His Savior

Steven Lewis

A T ELEVEN P.M., AFTER SEVEN TIE VOTES, AND AGAINST FATHER Mulcahey's distinct though unspoken wishes, Marj Cznepnicki was finally chosen to chair the Christmas organizing committee at Our Lady of the Lake Catholic Church. Triumphant but dignified, she and Joan Carswell, previously of Fond du Lac, walked directly down to the dank basement of the rectory and over to the wooden storage locker near the old coal-fired furnace.

With Marj waiting, hands on those heirloom slim hips, Joan nervously inserted key after key until she found the right one, yanked the rusted lock off, and pulled the creaking door open. Marj stepped in first, grabbed the dangling string, with its brass cross tied at the bottom, and tugged on the light. "Oh!" Joan grimaced, eyes instantly pooling.

"No," agreed the dry-eyed and tight-lipped chair of the organizing committee. "This just won't do." She picked up a tail-less, one-eyed papier maché donkey: "Look at this! And this—" dropping the donkey and pointing to a decapitated Wise Man, dusty head near fingerless hand, in the far corner.

"I'm sorry, Margie, I didn't—"

"Joan," Marj commanded, waiting for eye contact. The pleasantly chunky woman in her favorite seasonal pink velour ensemble, lifted her eyes without moving her head. "Get a grip, Joan, we're Catholics, not Gypsies. No one, least of all me, would think that you're responsible for this unholy mess!" She shook her head. "I mean, just what was that man thinking?" she scrunched her thin-as-her-hips lips together.

"Well, maybe, Margie, maybe since they began using the blow-up Nativity scene a couple of years ago, Father forg—"

"Don't be ridiculous—and besides, didn't you just move here in June, so what—?" She had no intention of finishing the sentence.

"I'm sorry, I just—"

"Well, don't *just*. I'll tell you what this is all about, since you're new to this grand old parish: it's about me trying to bring some elegance and tradition back to a beautiful cathedral. It's about Christ being under attack at the elementary school where you teach children to sing nondenominational songs. It's about me trying to elevate the birth of our Savior above some cartoonish plastic blow-up scene off the Disney channel. And it's about that senile old buffoon trying to make me look stupid for challenging him." She nudged a three-legged sheep and it fell over in a small cloud of dust. "And this manger! Look at this manger! It's dreadful. It looks like—, like—, like—, oh, I don't know what the hell it looks like!"

Joan concocted a frown on her face. "I guess you mean *h-e-double hockey sticks*, eh?" she said, and then smiled.

"No, Joan, I meant *hell*. This is hell. Look around."

As soon as the curtain dropped on the annual holiday (né Christmas) concert at LaFollette Elementary on the South Side of Milwaukee, Stanley Poniwascz, his dirty fingernails hiding his thin lips, leaned over to freckle-faced, strawberry blond Janie Goldenberg. "Ya know, it was Jews who nailed Christ."

Her dark-blue eyes widened. "No, you're wrong, Stanley Poniwascz," she whispered. "My daddy said it was the Romans, and he knows. He's the—"

"Yeah, I know all about your dad. My ma says he hates the baby Jesus."

"He does not!"

"Does too."

She closed her eyes just the way her mom does when Dad annoys her. "Does too."

"Well, he's the one on the school board who—"

"Who what?" she sneered.

"Who wrecked this whole stupid concert."

Just then Mrs. Carswell cleared her throat and enunciated very clearly, "Mr. Poniwascz and Miss Goldenberg!" Each stood red-faced, on the top riser, the girl taller than the boy, barely breathing as they waited for the choir teacher to turn her attention to dismissing Row 1. Stanley spoke out of the side of his mouth, "Did too."

"Did not," Janie hissed, just as Mrs. Carswell pointed a thick Polish sausage of a finger right at Gloria Robbins, who nodded and smirked, stepping off the riser and turning right. Girls were to turn right and boys were to turn left. Stanley stepped down, cranked his barbered head around, and mouthed, "Christ Killer" right in Janie's face.

She stuck out her tongue, but Stanley was already moving along in the boys' processional, parents still clapping.

Five minutes later, strapped into the backseat of their brand new silver Prius Hybrid, Janie asked her parents once again whether Jews had crucified Christ.

"Well," said the balding, tenured history professor at the state university, two hands on the steering wheel, "as I've told you in the past, Janie, technically it was the Romans, but the rabbis and other Jews were part of the group that demanded his death."

"Stanley Poniwascz said—"

"Stanley is just an uninformed boy who probably never met a Jewish person before you came into his class."

"Robert Green is Jewish."

"No, I'm afraid he's not. His father is Jewish, but his mother is Episcopalian."

"But Stanley Poniwascz—"

Janie Goldenberg's mother, who everyone always said must have stepped out of a Modigliani painting, turned her long, dark face toward Janie. "Stanley Poniwascz is descended from a long line of yeast-sucking Nazi dogs." And turning then to her husband, she muttered, "We never should have moved down here from Shorewood." An assistant professor in the English department at Marquette, Dr. Stein-

56

Goldenberg had recently announced to her husband and daughter at dinner, "I'm finished cleaning up after you two."

Dad shrugged and turned the radio on. "It doesn't really matter, Janie."

"Does too," she mumbled, squirming against the encroaching seatbelt and thinking now about that poor Christ in the stained-glass window at Our Lady of the Lake, nailed up there on the cross, blood dripping from his feet and hands. From her desk in Room 224 at LaFollette Elementary, she could see him staring across at her. Mrs. Carswell even pointed out the window one day and said it was the most beautiful vision she had ever seen.

"It doesn't matter, Janie," said Mom, looking out the passenger window.

Janie looked at the palm of her hand, trying to imagine what it would feel like to have a spike driven through it. "Does too."

"DOES TOO," Janie mumbled again an hour later, when her mom came into her room to kiss her good night.

"Yes, I love you, too, darling," her mom whispered. "Don't forget: tomorrow you need to clean your room and take care of that closet. I'm not your maid."

And what seemed hours later in the bright, rugless, moonlit room, but was probably only forty-five minutes, Janie finally heard her parents' bedroom door click closed. That was the sign that all was well, the click that meant that she could now safely fall asleep. She closed her eyes, but sleep would not come. Snuggling under her fluffy pink comforter and hugging her new Addy American Girl doll tightly in her arms, Janie was still wondering what it would feel like to have a spike driven through her hand.

Which was when she thought about Father Mulcahey. She knew the priest because he had stopped by one evening after her dad was elected to the school board. Also, Mrs. Carswell had invited him to visit her class a few weeks before to talk about the meaning of Christmas—and Janie, who wouldn't know a brogue if it took up residence in her throat, loved the soft sound around his voice, the way it flowed so smoothly through those crooked yellow teeth. He didn't sound like everyone else down there on the South Side, practically honking through their noses, as she once heard her mom say.

And so Janie decided then and there that she would stop in at the church right after vacation and tell Father Mulcahey, who seemed like a very kind man, that she was really, really sorry if the Jews had murdered Christ. And that even if they didn't do it, she was sorry anyway.

That made her feel much better, but five seconds later, which was probably five minutes, it seemed impossible to wait another second to tell him. This was too important, especially with only three days to go before Christmas.

So Janie Goldenberg slid out from beneath the warm pink comforter, put some clothes on over her pajamas, and, carrying her boots, tiptoed down the hall and down the carpeted steps, lifted her light-blue winter jacket off the hook, took her gloves and hat out of the sleeve, stepped into her boots, bundled herself up, unlocked the front door, and went out into the crisp, starry night.

Our Lady of the Lake was on the corner, just two blocks away—and four blocks from Lake Michigan. The church was all lit up as if it were daytime, and the spotlights peeking out of the frozen lawn made the crèche look all shimmery and bright. Everyone at school had been talking about how beautiful the living crèche was, but tonight the outdoor one was even more than beautiful to Janie, it was magical. Inside the white fence, on straw beds around the real wooden manger, were a real sheep, a real donkey, and a real pony.

Mrs. Carswell, who must have forgotten that Robert Green and Janie were Jewish, told everyone on the last day before vacation to bring their cameras to Mass on Christmas Eve because Mr. and Mrs. Cznepnicki would be dressing up as Mary and Joseph, and Mrs. Carswell's husband and two other men would come as the Wise Men, and, if it wasn't too cold, she beamed, Mrs. Miller's baby boy, Dylan, would lie in the manger, at least until he started crying.

In the meantime, she said, Mrs. Cznepnicki's beautiful antique alabaster-cheeked baby Jesus would be in the cradle. She held up a photograph of the doll, blue eyes wide open, staring at the heavens, peaceful, innocent, and serene.

Janie took one look at that gorgeous baby doll lying in the manger and, forgetting all about her speech to Father Mulcahey, opened the gate, and, stepping lightly around the sleeping donkey and sheep and pony, went over to the infant. She scooped up the baby Jesus in her arms just the way she had seen her Aunt Ruth pick up baby Sarah. Then she turned and tiptoed back out the gate and, walking as quickly as her skinny legs would move her, made it back to her house at 3379 South Linebarger Terrace, where she opened the front door without a sound, turned the lock, put the infant on a chair, took off her things, stuffed the mittens and hat into the arm of the coat, hung the coat on the hook, tiptoed up the steps, put the doll on her bed, took off her clothes, snuggled in under the covers, lifted her pajama shirt just the way Aunt Ruth did, and nursed the baby Jesus, humming, "Slee-eep in heavenly pea-eas, slee-eep in heavenly peas."

WHEN JANIE OPENED HER EYES to an orange sky the next morning, she smiled down at the infant still in her arms. She held her breath and listened for creaking floorboards, for a toilet flushing, for the hum of the shower. She sniffed deeply for that nose-scrunching smell of coffee dripping in the kitchen. And when she was a hundred and ten percent satisfied, as her dad often said, that her parents were still asleep, Janie Goldenberg kicked off the covers and stood up, her bare feet on the cold wood floor a sudden reminder of how badly she needed to pee.

But first she tiptoed over to her messy closet, made a nest out of some old sweaters that had fallen into the dusty corner, and laid the baby Jesus down. She covered him in last year's pink parka, put a Brewers baseball cap on his head, placed Addy next to him so he wouldn't ever be lonely, and pushed the thickly painted closet door shut. He would be safe there forever.

And as she sat down on the freezing-cold toilet seat, Janie Goldenberg smiled a smile she imagined to be as angelic as the smile of Mrs. Miller's baby, Dylan, who might be lucky enough to grow up and talk just like Father Mulcahey. ◇

The View from Pisgah

Mark Deitch

IT TOOK A WHILE FOR MAC TO GET READY. EVERYTHING TOOK A WHILE these days. Mac had to laugh, thinking of the heedless life he had led before; but now the old rage and reckless ways had been burnt right out of him. Now just preparing to go out was a concentrated campaign, like mustering an army. Water bottle from the cabinet. Healthy snacks from the fridge. Sun cap from the closet. Collapsible deck chair from the garage. After each excursion, Mac had to stop and rest, sit and let the oxygen soak back into his soggy lungs.

A last check of the pill box to make sure he was primed and ready to go. The water pill that made him pee all the time. The pill that urged his lazy heart to contract. The other pill that did something else and made him cough at night, a dry tickle on top of the wet heaves that came over him whenever he lay down.

Car keys. Where were the damned car keys? Mac scoured the usual hiding places, and by the time he found them, he had to pee again. After that, he needed a good ten minutes sitting at the kitchen table watching the squiggles swim in front of his eyes before he was steady enough to stand up again.

Mac used to be in a ferocious rush for everything, plowing head-on through life, with a trail of jobs and women broken and discarded in his wake. When he finally married it was late, in his forties, and the engines were still revving high for the first couple of years. It was touch and go for a while with him and Anita, and he didn't really start to change until Jerry was born. The very first time he held the tiny, squalling infant to his shoulder, Mac felt something hard release inside him and something else, warm and liquid, flow in to take its place. But then, just as he was edging his way into fatherhood and responsibility, wouldn't you know it? The old ticker turned on him, in revenge for all those years of overdrive.

It had happened the night of his fiftieth birthday party, a big barbecue in their backyard. He did his best to ignore it, shove it aside in the midst of the laughing and good times; but once the guests had gone he knew he would have to tell Anita. Jerry was asleep upstairs, and Mac didn't want to disturb him, so he was going to drive himself to the hospital, until Anita got in front of him, her back pressed against the door, and wrestled the keys out of his hand. And now here he was, two surgeries and five stents behind him, under a life sentence of plodding patience with the endless round of small obstacles that made up his day.

He drove slowly to the field, nosed into the parking lot, rolled up to the handicapped spot—his spot—right near the gate. But he was late, the lot was crowded, and his spot was taken. Mac hit the brakes and stared. He closed his eyes and opened them, but the fat, green SUV was still squatting between the blue lines. Catastrophe. His whole strategy in shambles. He knew that if he parked much farther away, he wouldn't have the wind to make it to the gate and then navigate the dreaded hill.

Mac wrestled his car around, drove down the line of vehicles angle parked on both sides of the narrow lot. No spots at all. No choice but to pull out into the street, out of his walking range. Down the block, he finally found an opening perilously close to a fire hydrant, but at this point he didn't care. It took him three tries and all of his waning strength to parallel park and pull up close to the vehicle before him. Spent, he draped an arm across the steering wheel and dropped his head to rest. The thought of another ambulance ride to the ER loomed, and the cold fear came over him. He slapped the dashboard weakly with his palm and fought back tears of frustration.

Mac became aware of a noise behind his ear, an irritating sound that wouldn't go away. He looked up, and a brown face swam into view, accompanied by a finger tapping at his side window. The mouth was open, white teeth talking to him. Mac pressed the button to lower the window.

"Mr. McIntyre, are you all right?"

Mac stared uncomprehendingly at the young man's face, with its bank of thick, black hair, the mouth moving, concern in the dark eyes.

"It's me, Victor Hermes. One of Jerry's coaches. Can I help you with anything?"

The world returned to ordered shapes and distinct colors. The boulder had lifted from his chest. Mac was aware of the sun, warm on his face and neck.

"Mr. McIntyre?"

"Victor," he said at last. "Do you have a car?"

VICTOR DROVE HIM into the parking lot, remarking how fortunate it was that he had been running late himself. He had had to park in the street, right across from Mac, and that's how Victor was able to find him as he sat napping in his car.

"A miracle," Victor said. Mac nodded and didn't bother to correct him about the napping.

"Jerry is a good boy," Victor said. "Very mature for his age. When is his birthday?"

"He turns twelve in November."

"That is good. We'll have him for another season. Maybe he can be captain next year. The other boys already look to him as a leader."

Mac flushed with pride. He tried to find something to say, settled for a mumbled, "Thank you."

They pulled up at the gate. Mac got out in front of the grassy hill overlooking the field.

"Do you need help getting up there?" Victor asked.

"No, thanks. I've got this one on my own."

Victor drove off to repark, and Mac contemplated the hill. Maybe twenty-five yards in total, but steep, too steep to tackle directly. If he stayed on the meandering path, it was a much longer but gentler incline. He could hear the noises down below. If he hesitated much longer, he might miss everything.

Mac started along the path, counting his steps. Twenty paces and a rest, then twenty more. Slow but steady. The late-afternoon sun dazzled his eyes, so he kept his head down, concentrating on the path ahead. When Victor had rescued him from the street, Mac, in his eagerness and gratitude had forgotten everything—the water bottle, his snack, the collapsible chair, his sunglasses and hat. If he somehow made it to the top, there would be no place for him to sit, no protection from the sun. No matter. He was down to fifteen paces between rests, then ten. He had forgotten to call Anita to tell her where he was going. If she got home from work early, would she worry? Would she be cross with him for venturing out and imperiling himself again? Another ten paces, then a miracle, the second of the afternoon. A bench on the side of the path, beckoning him.

Mac collapsed into its wooden arms. His shirt was soaked and he felt the wetness all the way through. This time he couldn't hold back the helpless tears. A man is more than ninety percent water, he thought, and I am dissolving, inside and out. The tears continued, but he was laughing now, his shoulders shaking as he wheezed.

The pulsing quieted in his ears and he stood up. Last lap, he told himself, the stretch run. Mac started up the path again. Ten steps. Eight. Then five. A soft wave of chattering sound washed over him.

Mac looked up, surprised to see that he was there—he had made it to the crest. The slanting sun blinded him, and he shielded his eyes with one hand. Down below, through the glare, the field blossomed into view, like the earth emerging from a cloudbank through the window of a jetliner. It was so suddenly beautiful he nearly sank to his knees. He took in the emerald expanse of the outfield, the symmetry of the white chalk lines stretching out from home and merging into the tall, yellow foul poles, which stood out against the even taller trees, their green boughs shimmying in the breeze. Small red jerseys dotted the field, frozen in their ready positions beneath oversized white caps. Mac sought out Jerry, one of the red jerseys, crouching intently at shortstop. On the bases were blue jerseys and black helmets, also frozen, leaning forward in arrested motion.

For a long moment the stillness held. Mac felt an eerie chill coursing up his spine, and then the pitcher broke the spell and delivered the ball. The batter swung and the white streak split the gap in left center. At once, the field exploded in color and motion as outfielders raced to converge on the ball, runners dashed around the bases, coaches yelled and pinwheeled their arms. Jerry sprinted out from shortstop to take the relay, and Victor Hermes was almost on the field himself, urging him to throw home. Both benches jumped and swarmed and shrilled.

Up on the hill, Mac saw it all through wet and increasingly distant eyes. He seemed to be observing from a great height and from very far away, as the little jewel box of a field continued to spin brightly, its tiny mechanism in constant, sparkling motion, as if this world of energy and action would never end. ◇

Night View

Linda Levitz

She savors those sweet extra moments
with her lover—Now it's late
Sandals clicking, she hurries along the dark
canal road—Yoko sent on ahead
In a patterned cloak clutched over her red
silk kimono, Lady Koriyama counts
the stars reflected in the canal, floating
past the paper lantern

Will she return with him in the spring?
stroll quietly, recite poetry?
View of the mountain, cherry trees, the water.
A snowy egret takes flight, noiselessly
lifts above her head
An omen—a message on the wing

She awaits his secret letter ◇

In the Old Days . . .

Linda Levitz

Foaming spume near the shore,
The gray whale senses our hunger
He heads for land, offers himself to us

A new rock washes up on the beach
With hooks and baskets, we run,
start a driftwood fire to rend the blubber,
sliced into huge cakes

Before the first cut, we thank the whale
for remembering us, gently close his moist eye
Birds and dogs demand their share
but we guard the meat
Four days and nights of slippery work

Our winter so hard, icy and long
Weeks of black nights
We need the warmth of the whale's meat and fat,
rendered oil for lamplight
His blood red and thick like ours

We teethe the blubber, our mouths
and lips slick with grease—Life!
Our children's bellies full
Thank you, brother ◇

Encomiast

David Carlyon

"Sukey in the Dark . . . the classical story of Eros and Psyche . . . There is comedy along the way, but this is a weightier piece . . . freighted with psychology . . . [and] an encomiastic quartet for the singers. A simple classical stone seat revolves . . . [A final moment] resolves the swirling complications of the relationship between our outer senses and inner souls."
—Opera review, *Philadelphia City Paper*, 2001

The psychology's freighted, the piece is weightier
　　And though there's comedy along the way
When Sukey and Eros grow matey-er
　　Levity's outweighed by gravity, so it's okay.
Yet as the quartet sings and the seat revolves
　　Question comes from the political enthusiast
As tension of inner and outer resolves
　　Are you now or have you ever been encomiast? ◇

The Pipeline

Kevin Egan

EVERY MORNING I CREEP DOWN TO THE LANDING THAT GRANDMA uses as a bedroom at the bottom of the stairs, and into the kitchen, where I try to eat breakfast without waking the house. The problem is Grandma always hears me and, before I can even get the milk pitcher out of the refrigerator, she's in the kitchen, too, her dark green bathrobe twisted crazily because she's wearing one sleeve inside out.

Grandma has this wonderful smile and a musical Irish brogue, which make you forget she can't be left alone because she'll "get into trouble." Mom spends the days with her, then hands her off to Dad when he gets home from the plant. On school mornings I need to get up real early to fit in breakfast and chores before the bus arrives. So in the mornings it's just me.

Grandma stands at the kitchen sink and runs a dirty bowl under the faucet. She's telling her old story about the cow her family owned when she was a girl. The cow's name was Anna Livia Plurabelle, and Grandma's job was to drive it from the barn to the field in the morning, then back to the barn in the evening.

"One evening, I arrived at the field to find a wee man, one of the gentle folk, in Anna's place. He told me his people had borrowed her and would have her back by morning. My Da would understand."

Grandma shuffles to the table and sets a bowl of corn flakes in front of me. Chocolate pudding still stains the rim. A long gray hair floats in the milk. Stifling a gag, I take my spoon in hand and wait for her to shuffle back to the chair by the window.

"I told my Da . . . " And as she tells me again how the gentle folk took Anna each night of the full moon and in return promised she never would run dry, I quietly scrape the cereal into the trash and set the bowl in the sink.

Outside, I zip my jacket to my Adam's apple. The calendar says spring, but the mornings still snap like winter. Back home there would be buds swelling on the trees, crocuses and onion grass sprouting on lawns. Here, when the sun breaks over the pipeline notch in the hill across the valley, all you see are gray trees and brown stubble fields.

I balance my schoolbooks on the mailbox and cross the road to refill the chicken feed and top off the water. Behind the coop, I slop out Bert and Harry's sty. Our cow boards down the road with a real farmer. Good thing, because the chickens and these two pigs are enough work for me. I wish a leprechaun would take them all away forever.

The school bus crunches to a stop, and I crawl into the last seat, where I always pretend to sleep while the bus fills up with hillbilly kids. Before I close my eyes, I look up at the house. Grandma is a silhouette at the kitchen window, still talking about her cow.

THE FIRST WARM SUNDAY we picnic in the field below the barn. Mom fixes the food and minds Grandma while Dad and I head for the pipeline. We've lived on the farm six months now, but with the bad weather and the long nights, this is our first climb.

At a distance, the pipeline looks like a swath of soft grass rising gently through the wooded hills. Up close, it's spiky scrub on a slope as steep as a ski jump. Dad lopes easily upward in long strides while I huff behind him. There is no pipe in the pipeline, he tells me. The power company predicts natural gas strikes in these hills, so it pays farmers a monthly fee for a right-of-way. The hillbilly kids talk about how they'll spend their money when gas blows on their land. But Dad just hopes that when the gas is struck, wherever it's struck, his company lands the contract for the pipe.

The slope levels off midway up the hill and we stop to rest. The valley is a patchwork of green, spring coming at different times to different corners. Below us, Mom and Grandma are two white specks on a red smudge of blanket. Dad clears his throat, and I know we've come to talk about my slacking off my morning chores.

I tell him I know the owners moved the plant to the cheap labor, but I can't understand why we bought a broken-down farm seven dirt-road miles from town. Back home, I could ride my bike wherever I pleased. Here I'm at the mercy of the school bus, the stones in the road cut the thickest balloon tires to ribbons, I don't know what I'll do for spending money come summertime, and everyone at school laughs at my funny accent. And whose idea were the animals anyway?

"The livestock came with the land," says Dad. "They are your responsibility until we sell them off."

But he promises to arrange a summer job in town and, if things work out financially, he might swing a second car. We are about to shake on this when I bring up Grandma's breakfast antics. Dad's expression turns somber. He reminds me how I would tag along to visit the convent where she lived as caretaker after Grandpa died, how she always slipped me a mint wrapped in cellophane.

"But I always find hair in the corn flakes," I say.

We don't climb the rest of the pipeline.

FOURTH OF JULY Dad throws a barbecue for people from the plant. Since he's middle management, he invites everyone from the owners right down to the guy who sweeps the floor. Their families come, too, and I recognize several kids from school.

I expect engineering types yapping about natural gas and scrambling over the pipeline to check out exactly how to lay the pipe. But no one mentions gas, no one even glances at the pipeline. Instead, everyone talks about a new contract with NASA for quarter-inch metal hoses the length of a finger. The hoses are bound for the space shuttle, which will take off like a rocket and land like an airplane. The engineering types gnaw on burgers, push their glasses back up their noses, elbow each other about VIP passes to lift-offs at Kennedy.

I steal around back of the house, where the Camaro Dad bought from the high school bio teacher sits on the dirt driveway. Five years old, it already shows the wear of country roads. Rust eats at the wheel wells. Tar stains the chrome of the grille. White stuffing erupts from a slit in the driver's seat. But I don't see the car with my eyes. I see it with my heart.

I mix a bucketful of soap. Tomorrow is my first day as counterman at the Rainbow Sweet Shoppe, and I want the Camaro to shine. I'm rubbing hard when I feel eyes burning into my back. I assume it's Grandma, because last I saw she was slouched in the old metal glider on the front porch, looking antsy with all the strangers milling around. But the eyes belong to a girl from school named Dovie, and for a moment I wonder why she's here until I remember her father works at the plant.

"That's Mr. Swartwood's car," she says. Mr. Swartwood is young and has a reputation for being cool.

"Used to be." I dunk my sponge and slop a huge mass of suds onto the roof. "It's mine now."

Dovie tiptoes across rivulets of water streaking the dirt driveway. She cups her hand and peers through the tightly closed windows. I first noticed her in English class, wearing a cheerleader's uniform for the junior varsity basketball game. She was cute, with dark hair pulled into a thick ponytail. Today she wears her hair loose and wiry, like the Jewish girls back home.

She circles the car, one hand on her chin. I wonder if she's fishing for talk or interested in the car. We never spoke in school, except to read parts from *High Tor*. Everyone snickered at my city accent that day, and even she bit her lip between lines. But I decide she digs the Camaro, so I let the car talk for me. I slop on more suds, squint one eye, rub hard through clusters of bubbles. All the time I bask in Mr. Swartwood's reflected coolness. When I look up, Dovie's gone back to the party.

I LIE IN BED, my finger nudging the dial of a transistor radio pressed against my ear. On cloudy nights, distant radio waves bounce low across the hills, and I can pull in Cleveland, Detroit, Chicago, even stations from back home. The static recedes, and the voice of a familiar deejay swirls into my ear. After one song, the signal wavers and then breaks up.

I've obsessed about Dovie for a solid week, stretching that two-minute encounter like a piece of taffy to examine every strand, wondering whether my silence blew a chance or saved me from foolishness. She passes the Sweet Shoppe each day and must see the Camaro parked nearby. But no teenagers dare hang out in the Shoppe till after dark, when I'm long back in the hills, grounded by a junior license. I can analyze this thing to death, I realize, so I decide to buzz to her house after work tomorrow and ask her on a date for Saturday afternoon. And the next day, when my shift ends, I haven't lost my nerve.

Dovie lives where the backyards tail off and turn into cornfields. A breeze sucks white curtains against a window screen. A radio tinkles deep inside. I knock on the door and step aside so she's certain to see the Camaro parked in front. She materializes in cut-off jeans and a tie-dyed T-shirt and greets me with a giggle. I barge right into my invitation. Buttermilk Falls. Saturday. She giggles again, and I pile on the details. Eleven a.m. Pack a lunch. Take my Camaro.

"Yes," she says, probably to save me embarrassment.

I'm so stunned that when she asks me in for lemonade I beat a hasty retreat.

WEDNESDAY NIGHT, a thud shakes the house. I creep to the heat grating in my bedroom floor and peer into the living room below. Light from the kitchen lays a bright trapezoid across the living room carpet.

I pad down to the bottom of the stairs and see Grandma isn't in her bed, which means she thinks it's breakfast time and I'll be eating corn flakes at ten past midnight. But the kitchen is empty, and the bathroom door is ajar. Inside, Grandma lies crumpled on the floor, a pool of blood spreading from her head.

I holler like a banshee.

The nearest hospital is thirty miles away, across a stretch of hills the locals call the Hogbacks. I always wondered about the name, but with Dad gunning the car into the dips and up the slopes and Grandma groaning in the back seat, I don't wonder anymore. It's past four when a doctor finally talks to us. Grandma's brain is addled, he explains. She believed she was getting into bed, let herself drop, and cracked her head against the toilet seat.

"Have you considered a nursing home?" he says.

"No, we haven't," says Dad.

BETWEEN SITTING AT THE HOSPITAL and running around buying medical equipment, I miss two full days of work. But finally Grandma is back in the house, along with bed rails and a shower seat. With her swollen chin and bandaged forehead, she looks like Popeye.

Saturday morning Mom and Dad spring a meeting with a social worker on me. Can't be changed. Will take up most of the afternoon. Someone needs to mind Grandma. I never told them about the date with Dovie, and I storm off to the phone, slamming doors in my wake. Dovie says she understands, but her parting giggle makes me think she never expected me to follow through.

Mom and Dad set Grandma up on the front porch with lunch, a pitcher of iced tea, and pillows for the glider. I'm to keep an eye on her and, when the sun swings around the house, drag the glider into the shade.

First time I call to Grandma through a window, her iced tea is gone, and flies spiral around the crusts of her sandwich. She doesn't answer, only stares across the valley and chews her tongue. After that, I just peek. She doesn't move, doesn't seem in any need. Finally, I head out the back door. The Camaro sits in the driveway, the sun baking a layer of dust into its metal hide. I yank out the hose, dump soap powder into a bucket, but I never turn the faucet. The car looks too dirty, like no amount of washing will ever rub it clean.

I dive behind the wheel. The hot vinyl singes my skin, but I let it burn. My infatuation with Dovie has pulled me through the last two weeks, and now nothing shields my hatred for this farm, these hills, the entire countryside. I should be at Buttermilk Falls with Dovie. Instead, I'm babysitting someone who doesn't even know I'm here.

I lie there in my funk long enough for the sun to move across the windshield. When I check on Grandma, I find the glider empty and hot as a frying pan. I scour the house and return to the porch, thinking maybe she melted into the pillows. Then something catches my eye from clear across the valley: a white dot slowly climbing the pipeline.

I race through the lower field, which is chest high and buzzing with insects. I slip under the barbed-wire fence marking the end of our land. Grandma still climbs, but I gain fast. Finally she stops midway up to sit on a rock. Huffing, I crash beside her. She doesn't notice, just stares back at the house and silently works her jaws. Red welts glisten on her ankles and burrs stick to her duster. I start to speak, but she cuts me off.

"Your father won't let me climb this hill, and now I know why."

"Because you'll kill yourself is why." I try lifting Grandma off the rock, but she doesn't budge.

"I needed to see for myself. I didn't think the pitch would be so steep."

"I could have told you that," I say.

A growl vibrates in my chest, then builds and separates into the engine of a car droning across the quiet of the valley. When conditions are right, you can hear a car miles off. Sometimes the car never reaches you, just fades back into the buzz of the insects. But down below a dust plume rises over the trees, and a car breaks out into a clear stretch between two fields.

"We'd better get back," I say. I try lifting her again, but it's like uprooting a tree.

The car swings up the driveway and parks next to the Camaro. Mom and Dad climb out and slam their doors, the sound reaching us three seconds later. I stand behind Grandma and work both hands under her arms, but she stays solid on the rock. A screen door bangs sharply, another of the sounds that carry across the valley. Dad ransacks the porch, then starts hollering for us.

"I'm sorry I ruined your day," says Grandma.

"You didn't," I say, which is a lie, of course, because all I want is to get her down the hill.

"I bet you had a date and then you needed to stay home with me."

I wonder whether Grandma really knows about Dovie, or if one of her notions accidentally hit the mark.

"He was the same way whenever a young girl got under his skin," she says. "The world stopped."

"That's not my big worry now," I say.

She cocks her head at me, as if waiting for me to dig into a bowl of corn flakes.

"I'm supposed to be minding you," I tell her.

Dad wades toward the lower field, waving his arms and shouting like he's spotted us. A smile blooms on Grandma's face as she listens to him yell.

"I'll handle him if you keep our secret."

"What secret?"

"About the farm. This isn't the farm in Ireland, but I don't want him thinking he failed me."

I lift again, and she rises easily upright. Dad still shouts. He sounded worried before, but now he sounds angry. Maybe because we're ignoring him, maybe because he snagged himself on some barbed wire.

"It's a beautiful farm just the same," Grandma says, leaning against me as we stagger down the steep, clumpy grass. "You know, we had a moo cow at the old farm. Anna Livia Plurabelle."

We aren't on the pipeline anymore. We're back in a world where leprechauns borrow cows on the night of the full moon. She tells the story again, and it sounds fresh, if only because she tells it without missing any of the details I know like an old song. ◇

The Notes of Delirium

Lya Ferreyra

Lya Ferreyra's "The Notes of Delirium" was the winner of this year's mystery-writing contest for middle- and high-school students, held in connection with EVERMORE, *the Rye Arts Center's annual event celebrating Edgar Allan Poe. Now in its third year—and Poe's 200th—the contest, organized by Maureen Amaturo, encourages young Westchester authors to write "in the spirit of Poe." Lya's entry was the number-one choice of all three judges: the memoirist and teacher Lee Stringer, the thriller writer Ira Berkowitz, and the mystery novelist Alan Beechey, for "truly capturing Poe's world of fear, obsession, and the macabre."*

TIMOTHY BRANCH AWOKE AS THE CLOCK STRUCK MIDNIGHT. He quietly got out of bed, careful to not wake his wife, who lay sound asleep. Her soft breathing accompanied him as he slowly got dressed and tiptoed down the stairs. Once he had left the house a new energy overtook him, and his pace became increasingly brisk. Coming to a sudden halt, he hid behind a tree. Footsteps were becoming audible, and it was not long before Jeremiah Smith came into view. His long, gaunt face cried out for a shave, and his shabby coat hung pathetically from his skinny frame. Jeremiah had once been a successful farmer, but his fondness for gin had soon laid all his hard work to waste. The death of his wife, Milly, had not helped in the least.

Milly had been twenty years her husband's junior and had possessed a shy, somber composure. The couple had never been one for public affection. It had seemed to Timothy a loveless marriage, yet when she died from pneumonia, Jeremiah had been inconsolable. He would cry out her name during one of his numerous drunken stupors, and it was rumored that he had preserved the body in his cellar in a sort of shrine. Timothy was not inclined to believe town gossip; in his opinion Jeremiah was a man who had always wanted the unattainable, and what is more unattainable than someone beyond the veil of death?

The creaking of the cemetery gate brought Timothy back to the present. Jeremiah seemed to be in a trance as he frantically walked toward his decrepit family crypt. As Timothy followed Jeremiah, he grew increasingly excited. He would finally put an end to the gnawing curiosity that had haunted him. It had begun about a month ago, when Timothy had awoken to the slam of a door. He had witnessed the old man rush toward the cemetery every night since then. It had become a steadily growing obsession. He began to wonder for the first time if there was some truth to the town rumors. Tonight was the first night he had been compelled to follow the source of his torment.

Jeremiah was now entering the crumbling crypt, the padlock that had once kept the dead locked away had been broken long ago. Frantic shadows were cast across Jeremiah's face, turning his excited smile into an eerie grimace. As Timothy entered the crypt, a wave of stale air engulfed him. Quick to hide behind a column, he observed Jeremiah carefully lighting a conspicuous candle. A soft glow emitted from the wick, revealing the vision that lay on a large gray stone slab. It was Milly Smith. Her hair was dark and glossy, resembling liquid from afar. Her skin was so pale it seemed to cast a halo around her perfect petite body. Violet and blue roses bloomed all along her arms and below her delicate lashes. She did not move, she did not breathe, seeming to bask in her stillness. Jeremiah's eyes appeared black and devilish in the candlelight. He spoke to Milly in a hushed, reverent tone as his calloused hands brushed the outline of her lip and the curve of her cheek.

Timothy looked on, caught with an immense sense of awe at the stunning creature that lay not ten feet before him. How she had changed in death! Her mousy looks long gone, and meekness vanished. Jeremiah was a lucky man indeed. Still entranced, Jeremiah began to dance with what seemed like air, but soon Timothy could hear the wild notes of a distant rogue orchestra and perceive the outline of Milly, resting in Jeremiah's arms, her silhouette casting a shadow on the tomb walls. From a hole in the crypt roof, an old black crow cackled at the foolishness of man.

In search of the terrible music that flooded him, Timothy bolted from the crypt and soon found his way out of the cemetery. The music grew louder and louder as he ran. The sound drew him toward his home and finally to his own bed. His wife, Mathilde, still lay asleep. He had once thought her beautiful, but the raging music made him see her clearer than ever before. Her skin was red, and ugly veins pulsated beneath it like wriggling snakes. Her face, which had begun to wrinkle, reminded him of a rotting apple just past its prime. Agh! And her breathing, that loud boorish sound that escaped her every minute. She was never still, jittering and twitching like the lowliest of insects. It was enough to drive a man mad.

The terrible music grew louder and louder and Timothy ever more desperate. His hands locked around her neck, creating an exotic necklace fit for a queen. Mathilde's eyes popped open, wide with disbelief, as she vainly gasped for air. Timothy squeezed tighter and tighter until he could feel her neck crush beneath his hands. Heaving from the strain of righteous murder, he looked down at his rejuvenated bride. How striking she was in death. Silent. Still. Perfect. ◇

Dying Bouquet

Seth Appel

He often thinks of falling.
Of rain drops falling for so very long
    before hitting the earth,
or of a stone falling off an old bridge
and then disappearing into the waters beneath.
He finds comfort in that short moment
when an object is adrift in space, neither above nor below.

In the evenings he closes his book
and goes out to wander in the street.
He pretends that he's on his way to visit a dear friend,
or in a hurry to tend to an important task.
He wonders if strangers can see
the long gray robes that drag behind his feet.

One day he steps out of his home
and upon hearing a strange noise from within
peers through the keyhole to look back inside.

And there he sees himself sitting wordlessly
clutching a bouquet of dying flowers
in his wooden hands. He goes back inside
and together they dig up all the floors of their home
and inscribe their unfulfilled hopes and weary prayers
on the underside of the brick tiles.

In a rage they rip the library to shreds
and stuff the pillows and mattresses
with pages torn from philosophy books
and an old encyclopaedia. With a Bible
they line the bottom of the cupboards and cabinets.

Much later he carefully replaces all of the tiles,
and goes out to walk in the street. "Flowers!"
he keeps muttering. "Flowers!" ◇

Iron Lung

Lisa Fleck Dondiego

Paralyzed from the neck down as a result of childhood polio, Martha Mason
died at her home in Lattimore, N.C. She was seventy-one and had lived for
more than sixty years in an iron lung.

—The New York Times, May 10, 2009

My Siamese twin, it went everywhere I did.
Like the souvenir magnets from faraway friends
that covered its surface,
it stuck to me.
I couldn't get loose.

Breathless, I submitted to its grip,
my world horizontal. My head
stuck out, my eyes ravened books.
I wrote memoirs in that head,
sentence by sentence.

So tightly held,
how could I become enraged or weep—
or call this rescuing lover 'iron,'
whose only will was to keep me alive?
No, it lent me patience—
breath by breath—
imposed its rhythm of ins and outs
like a crepuscular tide, and then,
like a muscular lifeguard, kept dragging me back,
only to dive in again and again.

In the end, I burst from its long embrace,
gulped Heaven. ◇

Couple with Their Heads Full of Clouds

—Salvador Dali

Mary Lou Butler-Buschi

The other night
I was tending
peppers in the desert.
You were shaping
a table
made of sand.
The peppers, still young,
had no sign of fruit.
Your table, made of sand,
held for a while. ◇

What Bo Didn't Know

Joseph P. Griffith

REMEMBER THE OLD NIKE COMMERCIALS WITH THE ATHLETE BO Jackson, and the slogans "Bo knows football," "Bo knows baseball," and so on? Bo knew a lot of things, mainly how to make money, and after he suffered career-ending injuries, he didn't even have to play anymore to make it. He just picked up enormous checks based on what he used to do. All Bo needed to know at that point was how to count.

For every Bo who knows what it's like to make it, there are ten thousand who never reach the top. They exist only as playground legends, maybe getting a fleeting reference somewhere to attest to their athletic brilliance, but mainly commemorated through word of mouth. Aficionados and asphalt warriors will recognize the names. The Goat. Helicopter. Jackie Jackson. I never played against those people—hell, I couldn't even have stood on the same court with them—but back in Brooklyn in the 1960s I did know a few who played with and against them. They were playground legends, too.

There was Mickey, a ballhandling magician who specialized in the art of misdirection, firing passes to the open man with uncanny accuracy. Harry, a tall, lanky youth with enormous hands and an unerring shot. Stanley, a short, chameleonlike backcourtman with quick hands, a set of pop eyes in front, and an extra set in back. Whitley, a smooth forward who seemed not to sweat as he floated through the tightest defenses for easy layups. And Ack, the most complete playground ballplayer I've ever seen, a superaggressive competitor who, at a mere six feet, could defend like Bill Russell, drive like Elgin Baylor, and dazzle like Earl Monroe. Ack could not merely jump—he could fly.

But for sheer power, if you wanted to win, the man to have on your side was a different Bo. He was six-foot-three, two hundred pounds, with exaggeratedly bowed legs that propelled him like a rocket and probably accounted for his nickname. He had huge hands that slammed together with frightening strength for a rebound, and a big, flashing grin.

On the rare occasions when these guys played on the same team, it was an unbeatable combination, an awesome machine far greater than the sum of its parts, capable of destroying opponents with the same intensity as the New York Knicks, who were in the midst of their first championship season. You don't see teamwork like that anymore, at Madison Square Garden or on the playing fields of Brooklyn. Most guys are doing a solo performance and getting paid an obscene amount of money for wearing some overpriced sneaker logo.

While the Knicks were playing before capacity crowds, the young guys in our park on Aberdeen Street were establishing a reputation in neighborhoods throughout Bushwick and Bedford-Stuyvesant, but they never won mention in any newspaper. The real fame went to neighborhood names like Gotti and Gleason and Serpico; Eddie Egan of "The French Connection"; Batman and Robin, the "Super Cops"; Vince Edwards, "Ben Casey"; and the Yankees' former Rookie of the Year, Bob Grim, who owned a local bar. There was still a tight community of old guys who played bocce—nobody ever seemed to mess with them—but the WASPs and Bund members and wealthy brewers who'd gotten streets named after people like Pulaski, Kosciuzko, Lafayette, and DeKalb were long gone.

Somebody once told us that Bo and Ack were going head-to-head at a below–street-level schoolyard, whose backboard was visible from the street, and we ran over to see this clash of titans. As I approached

I could see their hands flashing by, about a foot from the top of the backboard, some thirteen feet up. These were people who leaped so high they could dunk two basketballs on the same trip up, in rapid succession; or dunk one, catch it with the other hand, and slam it through again before coming down. It took the NBA years to catch up to the tricks being done in many playgrounds, and the kind of maneuvers that are now a regular part of the NBA Slam Dunk Contest were old hat in my old neighborhood.

You're probably saying, "Aw, go on, you're making it sound better than it was. We saw plenty of good ballplayers, too, probably just as good or better." Okay, then, I'm going to tell you what set my friends apart. In particular, Bo.

It's become a cliché for people to talk about how they survived bad neighborhoods and how all their friends ended up dead or in jail. The fact is that, as the only white boy in the neighborhood, I got my butt kicked, on and off the court, on a regular basis. To his credit, Bo never took part in all this, and even occasionally defended me for having the courage to stand there and take the verbal and physical abuse. He wasn't what I'd call a well-informed guy but, like anybody else, he had opinions and didn't hesitate to give them. He was pretty tough but he had that infectious grin and a keen sense of humor. I hardly ever saw him fight anyone—not many people were stupid enough to challenge him—but on the one or two occasions I did, he left his opponents raw and bloody. He did the standard in-your-face shtick but it was pretty low-key, because there was one thing Bo knew—he was going to win.

That's why there was no hesitation about traveling to the Pink Houses project in East New York for a New York City Housing Authority basketball clinic one summer morning in 1970, a few weeks after the Knicks had won their first NBA title. It was rumored that Walt Frazier, Clyde himself, would attend. There would undoubtedly be throngs of people there just to see the league's premier defensive player and fashion plate.

On the morning of the clinic I arrived early but the playground was deserted. After about a half-hour no one had shown up, and I was beginning to think the clinic had been canceled. Suddenly a jeep drove up, the doors opened, and the longest pair of legs I'd ever seen emerged. The figure unfolded in sections and drew up to its full height. It was the Knicks' Nate Bowman, The Snake, six-foot-ten and the backup center to the NBA's Most Valuable Player, Willis Reed. All season long I'd seen Wilt Chamberlain, Lew Alcindor (later Kareem Abdul-Jabbar), Wes Unseld, Elvin Hayes, and the other giants at the Garden, but it had been like watching a bullfight from the stands. This time I was going to be in with the bull.

More long legs emerged. They belonged to Dave Stallworth, the Knicks' six-foot-seven reserve forward who had been Bowman's teammate at Wichita State, and Fred Crawford, the Milwaukee Bucks' six-foot-four forward who had shared the court with Alcindor and run the legendary Rucker Tournament in Harlem. They were soon joined by the Boston Celtics guard Emmette Bryant and Bobby Hunter of the Harlem Globetrotters, who was known as "Never-Miss" Hunter, for obvious reasons. Even though Clyde was a no-show, it was a veritable dream team of the streets.

A crowd gathered and players signed up. It quickly became obvious that the only clinic to be held would be one in which all the "young boys" were taught a lesson. Bo arrived with another friend from the neighborhood. Three squads were formed to play half-court five-on-five against the pros; we picked up two locals and watched as the NBA stars quickly demolished the first two teams. "Oh, well, at least we can say we played against 'em," said Bo, taking what would surely be the inevitable in stride.

At last it was our turn. In situations like this there is an abject fear, an emptiness that resides in the pit of your stomach. I knew it was going to be bad; I think the fear was more of being embarrassed than of losing. The game proceeded and they scored a few quick baskets, but we answered with some of our own. It was quickly apparent that we were the best of the three local teams, which wasn't saying much. You rise to the level of the competition, though, and we found ourselves playing inspired ball, perhaps better than we ever had. I don't remember too much about the game, but there is one thing I will never forget.

Being, at five-ten, the third tallest member of our team, I found myself guarding Stallworth, giving away nine inches and seventy pounds in the process. As he stood in the low post and I peered out from behind him, I was fully aware of the irony. After all, just weeks before, a million Knicks fans and I had watched and hoped against hope as he stood in the same position in the hole, guarding Chamberlain in the fifth game of the finals against Los Angeles after Willis Reed had gone down with a torn thigh muscle. We had written off the game and the championship without The Captain, but somehow a miracle had occurred: Against incredible odds, Stallworth and Dave DeBusschere had combined to hold off the Dipper and win the game. By the time Reed returned, like the fallen Cid, to vanquish the Lakers in Game 7, it almost seemed anticlimactic.

I recalled the thrill of seeing Stallworth play perfect defense against Chamberlain, and I dug in my heels and leaned on him to try and keep him away from the basket. My most fervent hope was that he wouldn't turn around, because if he made up his mind to go to the basket, I was done.

It happened in a blur. Someone, maybe Bryant or Hunter, passed in to Stallworth. I was ready and stuck a hand in front of him to deflect the ball, then scrambled around him and dribbled. Out of the corner of my eye I saw Bo heading to the basket, and without thinking or looking I fired a lightning pass to him. I looked up to see him begin his leap from outside the free-throw lane. At the same time, Stallworth turned from me, on Bo's heels, and also leaped. In an instant Bo was in the air, his elbow above the rim, palming the ball like a grapefruit. From the opposite side came Bowman, lanky and angular, his arms unfolding like an eagle's wings, his armpit above the basket. I didn't have time to mutter what I was thinking: Bo's gonna get killed.

But I didn't know what Bo knew—and neither did they. I couldn't see his face, but maybe they did. Maybe they saw the fire of a true competitor in his eyes. Maybe they envisioned a summer wasted because of a stupid playground injury. Whatever it was, Nate Bowman and Dave Stallworth, members of the 1970 World Champion New York Knickerbockers, backed off.

Holy Christmas, he's gonna do it, I thought. But he didn't. Instead of the powerful dunk we expected, he turned his palm up in a gesture of mock submission, and dropped the ball through the hoop, light as a feather. There was silence in the park—Bo's successful challenge had stunned the crowd, followed by a roar that rose like the cheers in the Garden. Bowman, gawky and foul-prone but who had occasionally outplayed Alcindor; and Stallworth, the All-American; and Dave the Rave stood stonefaced, then grudgingly patted him—and said, "Nice move, man." The game stopped while our team mobbed Bo, hugged him, and slapped five.

We were energized and played some of the fastest, most adept ball we ever did, or probably ever would. But of course, the pros quickly proceeded to dismantle us before it got any more embarrassing for them. We took pride and satisfaction in having given them the best game of the three squads, and at having had the chance to play against some of the best.

After the game I said to Bo, "Why didn't you dunk it?"

That's when I found out another thing Bo knew. "I didn't want to make 'em mad," he said. Anybody else would have seized the moment and the glory, becoming known for that one kamikaze move before all hell broke loose. Bo knew enough not to embarrass them, to spare himself and us the embarrassment that would surely have followed.

I learned plenty about basketball from Bo. I wish I could have taught him something in return, for what Bo didn't know was how to continue his success off the court. If he could have channeled that intensity he could have made it to the pros. After all, he was much taller than Nate Robinson and plenty of others who made it. But through weakness, perhaps, or bad influence, or his own personal demons, he turned instead to heroin, and then to crime to support his habit. I never saw him do anything illegal aside from using drugs, but he was increasingly rumored to be involved in armed robberies. Finally, one day, came the news that he had tried to hold up a barber shop and been shot six times in the stomach. He was so strong that he was said to have crawled on his hands and knees for two blocks before he died. He was nineteen years old.

There are a hell of a lot of athletes out there who didn't know Bo, and don't know anything about how lucky they are. Seeing somebody like him laid out in a suit and tie for the first and last time ought to be required viewing for them. Maybe then the sports pages would return to being about sports, instead of about greed, drug arrests, suspensions, steroids, rape charges, dogfighting, and other violations of the law, ethics, and good taste. Until then, in the tradition of the old neighborhood, let me raise a toast to the dear departed and the boys upstate and all the guys like Bo who never made it. And now, let me drink the rest, to keep it from corrupting those who do. ◇

The Garden Plot

A. H. Block

AS YOU KNOW, I'M PARTIAL TO FLOWERS. BUT SUCH A MIXED-UP mess!" Miss Peggy Cowen, first floor rear, a bright floral-print smock covering her ample self, accosted the Warrens as they descended the stairs. "Coordination. That's what's needed. Mutual enhancement without trampling individuality. And the weeds!"

"You might be right," Beth Warren said, "but from our window it blends together beautifully."

"Particularly if you squint," said her husband, Adam. "But who cares about a bunch of flowers? Now vegetables . . . "

The subject under discussion by Mr. Harold Parrott's tenants was the backyard garden of his Horton Street brownstone. Without pattern, flowers pushed through in a continuous cacophony of colors: lavender and gold crocuses and pure snowdrops in early spring, followed by narcissus; tulips of myriad hues; violets and vivid Johnny-jump-ups; yellow, orange, and red lilies; marigolds, sweet william, portulaca, and impatiens; asters, and, finally, the saffron and rust of the chrysanthemums in autumn. From the Warrens' third floor apartment, it tinged the visual senses in a tangle of chroma and weeds.

"Your husband may pretend to be a Philistine, but he knows what I mean."

"It's obviously what Mr. Parrott likes, "Adam said. "He doesn't care about offending anyone's sense of order."

"He doesn't even realize it. He needs help. Suggestions. Positive criticism. And now, before he breaks ground."

"Then tell him."

"I thought we could make it a joint venture."

The memory of previous joint ventures, and the torturous maze of the discussions, bedeviled Adam. His inability to master the landlord's quirky reasoning frustrated him, as Mr. Parrott's mastery was achieved with deft unpredictability rather than with overpowering rationality. "Neat flowers aren't worth it," he said.

"I'm sure Anne and Hans would help," said Miss Cowen, referring to the Rugers, on the second floor.

"Then you don't need me," Adam said. "It's a waste of time. He won't pay attention and posies aren't that important. If you want to get excited about something, try vegetables."

"Oh, Adam," Beth said, "you are acting like a Philistine."

"Can a Philistine appreciate the beauty of a sunlit cornfield swaying with the breezes? Or the taste of a fresh-picked ear? Peas right off the vine and just-cut-asparagus? The contrast of a dead-ripe tomato against the green of its stalk? This Philistine could go on and on."

"Positively poetic," said Miss Cowen.

"Like a Parrott greeting card," Adam said.

Miss Cowen and Beth launched their campaign. First they mailed an article entitled "City Garden" to their landlord. Then, daily, an appropriate picture from Miss Cowen's collection of garden magazines and seed catalogues slipped under Mr. Parrott's door. A lack of reaction fueled their intensity.

Searching through their record collections, they culled Merman's version of "Everything's Coming Up Roses" and Tiny Tim warbling "Tiptoe Through the Tulips." The Rugers agreed to play them on their multi-speakered sound system, with the apartment door open.

"I would have selected something else," said Adam.

"I would like an opinion to state," said Hans Ruger. "Why do we pussyfool around? I prefer the direct approaching."

"Pussy*foot*, dear," said Anne. "With some people the direct approach works, not with Harold. But I'd like to hear what Adam would've picked."

"Oh, how about 'I'm A Lonely Little Petunia in an Onion Patch' or that 'tomahto/tomato, potahto/potato' thing."

Miss Cowen waved a chubby finger. "Adam, you have a disruptive soul."

THE MUSIC BLARED SPORADICALLY during the weekend. Late Sunday afternoon Miss Cowen said, "He's softened up."

"All you've done is given him time to set his defenses," said Adam. "You may have piqued his curiosity. Softened? No."

"Not in the accepted sense," Miss Cowen said, "but he'll realize that the prelims are over. My place, tonight at seven."

Five tenants and a landlord assembled in an apartment redolent with the bouquet of home-baked chocolate-chip cookies and freshly brewed coffee. Miss Cowen steered the get-together on course.

"Did you enjoy the music, Harold?"

As Mr. Parrott sipped, Adam slid back his chair, distancing himself from the others. Squinting his pale-blue eyes, their landlord scanned the group. "Could it be the kind of music that inspired the line 'I don't know much about it, but I know what I like'?"

Hans leaned forward. "You are liking it?"

Anne placed her hand on his shoulder. "Harold is being sarcastic, dear."

"So what are you thinking of it?"

"Even with the door closed I couldn't keep that screechy soprano with the ukulele out of the apartment. I can only conclude that something so bombastic was done for a purpose."

"Irving Berlin said, 'Say It with Music,'" said Miss Cowen.

Mr. Parrott popped a cookie into his mouth. "Say what?"

"Anything," Beth said. "Longfellow wrote, 'music is the international language of mankind.'"

"Like Esperanto," Anne said. "It does away with political and geographic borders."

"Ah," said Mr. Parrott, the corners of his mouth rising as he fixed the tenants in his gaze. "Imagine. Music doing away with my boarders."

"Anne, what says everyone. Why not the direct approaching?"

"Because," Miss Cowen said, "the fat lady hasn't sung."

"And when she does …?" said Mr. Parrott.

"It'll be music to your ears," said Beth.

Mr. Parrott nodded. "Perhaps. But it might have been more appropriate to suggest that it would soothe the savage beast."

From behind Beth a voice broke in. "Breast. Soothe the savage breast."

Adam, with an automatic reaction to the misquote, pushed his chair farther back, glanced at Beth, and shrugged. Then, as if in the clutches of Svengali, his eyes were drawn to Mr. Parrott, whose stare already bored into him.

"Well, Mr. Warren. You've found your tongue. I was sure you had laryngitis."

Adam cleared his throat. "I'm here for dessert. Nothing more."

"But we know you thrive on challenging conversation. Welcome."

"I haven't entered in."

"By blurting 'breast' you have."

"Just said in the interest of accuracy."

"Aha. You assumed I was quoting. By paraphrasing I was simply being self-deprecating. We landlords are often thought of as beasts."

"But a beast would never tend a garden," said Beth. Adam turned with admiration toward his wife, whose intervention not only provided a reprieve but, as usual, with understated sense and impeccable timing, restored order.

"Beauty's keeper had a garden," Mr. Parrott said.

Beth leaned in Mr. Parrott's direction. "And inside was love and gentleness."

The calm voice caused a stillness, as they all considered the status of the discussion. It seemed obvious that the next utterance would determine its direction.

"Anne! What do they talk about?"

Grasping Hans by the arm and searching Miss Cowen's face, Anne said, "Peggy?"

"Okay. Time for my aria. Surprise, Harold. It's your garden. As much as we admire your effort, we feel that it could be greatly improved with our input."

"It could be greatly improved without your input."

"So you agree it can be better."

"I believe I just did."

"Finally! The direct approaching *und* it works."

Mr. Parrott surveyed the room. "Am I to infer that the reason for all the paper under my door and the noise in my head was because you didn't want to come right out with it? Am I that much of a 'breast'? Mr. Warren, what do you think?"

Adam fidgeted. "I'm not involved."

"I find that uncharacteristic. You must have an opinion."

"*Ja*, he does."

Both Adam and Mr. Parrott faced Hans, a trace of a smile twitching the landlord's face and a scowl on Adam's. "And what is it?" asked Mr. Parrott.

"He would different music play. Somethings about onions, potatoes, and tomatoes."

"That's all?"

Adam moved forward. "Oh, what the hell! I would have said how lousy the produce is at the supermarket and how it's a shame you don't use that patch of dirt to grow some vegetables."

"Now there's a position. Convince me."

"If you haven't experienced the difference between store-bought and fresh-picked, I probably can't. If you have, it isn't necessary."

"Well, I have and it is. But I'm flabbergasted that you came here with no unanimity about the garden's function."

Adam scratched at a nonexistent itch on the underside of his left wrist. "There is a consensus."

"And you disagree. You owe us the benefit of your reasoning."

Adam glanced about the group, silent since the onset of the head-to-head encounter. Other than a smile of encouragement from Beth, he recognized in the expressions of the others a willingness to be passive witnesses to what they all sensed was the endgame. The itch moved behind his left ear. "I've stated my preference. There hasn't been a groundswell of support for it."

"Don't you care to promote your position?"

"That's right. I don't care to. It's not that important and ..."

"Why argue with someone so stubborn and inflexible."

"I didn't say that."

"That's true. But would you say I give no quarter?"

"Yes. You certainly give no quarter."

"But I do."

Adam shook his head; a definitive response to his tormentor, who broke into a broad grin, obliterating all but slits of the sparkling paleness in his eyes. "I'll prove you wrong by giving quarter—a quarter of my garden to Miss Cowen, a quarter to the Rugers, and a quarter . . ."

The eruption prevented him from finishing. Whooping laughter, applause, and exclamations of delight surrounded the beaming landowner, warmed by his tenants' pleasure and the exhilaration of verbal conflict. Adam slumped in grudging admiration.

"Harold," Miss Cowen said, holding up her cup, "the fat lady sang, but you took care of the encore. What are your conditions?"

"Do whatever you want."

"I guess this makes us your tenant farmers," said Anne.

"Yes. Except Mr. Warren. In view of his preference, he'll be a sharecropper. We all look forward to the harvest."

Planning commenced. The Rugers decided to create a rose garden, while Miss Cowen declared for sunflowers, hollyhocks, and gladioluses. The Warrens split their section, Adam selecting peas, followed by tomatoes and corn, and Beth choosing a varied display of annuals, picked more for their colors than their species. Mr. Parrott announced that he would continue as before except to be more diligent with his weeding.

MR. PARROTT'S AREA FLOWERED FIRST, as the spring bulbs popped through. The Rugers' bushes leafed out and Miss Cowen's seeds began their green ascension. The peas in Adam's section twined up and Beth's formal arrangement began to take shape. By June the entire garden bloomed, with the flowerless left rear corner providing the first edible crop of the season; two servings each of sugary peas for all but the Warrens, who, exercising their rights of possession, ate three. Plant rotation, necessary only for Adam, allowed the smooth transition to two new crops. They flourished with a hardiness that heightened the whetted appetites of 89 Horton Street. The appearance of small flaxen blossoms on the tomato stalks drew inspection by Mr. Parrott.

"Why have so many fallen off?"

Adam had ignored the yellow flecks under the plants. "I don't know, but I hope it's normal."

"I don't think it is. And those big green caterpillars?"

"Where?"

"There. Two . . . no, three."

Adam scrutinized the patch, seeking the fat horned invaders, nearly invisible on the vines they savored. "There're dozens! They're destroying my tomatoes!"

Mr. Parrott wandered toward the front of the garden, his "Maybe music will soothe the savage beasts" sign hanging unnoticed by the plucking and stomping Adam. Also unnoticed was the floral shower each time he snatched a spongy creature.

Not a single tomato ripened. The few that formed succumbed to a fungus, so Adam turned his energy to what remained—twelve tasseled plants bearing thirty-two finger-sized cobs. Regularly, he counted them, inspecting each for bore holes or yellowing, for nibbled silk. He gained confidence from the plumping of the ears and the darkening of the soft, moist strands protruding from them. One day, he caressed several and, feeling fullness under the husks, made an announcement.

"Tomorrow will be the day, Beth. Pass the word."

That evening he peered down from the kitchen. A light breeze had kicked in, stirring the stalks into a uniform swaying. In the quietness that surrounded him, he heard their faint crinoline rustle.

"Isn't it incredible, Beth?"

She stood beside him, nodding. "A touch of Iowa in our own backyard."

The view from the window the next morning elicited a bellowed

"Beth" before Adam pounded down the stairs and out the back door. Panting, he halted at his tenderly nurtured plot, stupefied by the aftermath of havoc. Stalks, denuded of every ear of corn, lay bent and twisted in a mockery of the neatness that once existed. Staring at the ravage, he became aware that everyone else had joined him. Beth took his hand and they stood several moments before he spoke.

"Who . . . how . . . ?"

"Maybe someone who needs it more than we do," she said.

"But who would know it was here? The neighbors? I can't believe that they . . ." Incomprehension overwhelmed Adam.

"Maybe some raccoons." Mr. Parrott spoke with authority.

"Not here," Adam said, unable to accept the unlikely while the unthinkable lay before him.

"They're here. I see them when I walk the dogs at night. They come up from the storm drains. Farmers believe they know when the corn is ripe."

"Well," Adam said, "whatever or whoever made sure there wasn't any left for us." He sighed. "I'm going to work."

"I'll fix you a nice breakfast," said Beth.

Although the flavor of sausage and pancakes soon faded, they provided a continuing comfort throughout the day, aiding Adam's innate resilience to take over. On his way home, he assessed the results of his first challenge of nature; a success, two setbacks, but one season's valuable knowledge. His thoughts raced ahead to the precautions he would take next year, instilling a surge of optimism that carried him bounding up two flights of stairs.

Next to the apartment door stood a large grocery bag, its sweet aroma identifying the contents before he looked inside. Among the ears nestled a note. Beth joined him at the kitchen table as he read aloud the penciled words of their landlord, the free-lance greeting-card poet:

> When urbanite raccoons parade
> and pull their nasty deeds,
> one kind of succor is farm aid
> (not in the form of seeds).

Accept this corn. Enjoy an ear
without your normal glowers.
Perhaps you'll do it right next year
by growing only flowers.

Adam's smile was involuntary. "I was thinking about next year, too. But not about flowers. Maybe he's right. It would certainly spare me some heartache."

"You have plenty of time to think about it. But right now, I'm going to start the water. You can husk."

"I'll change first."

As he passed into the living room, cries of "Surprise!" resounded. Surrounding him stood the Rugers, Miss Cowen, and, wearing a black domino mask and a ring-tailed hat, Mr. Parrott. In the next moments of laughing confusion, with Beth at his side, he experienced the wonder of witnessing one's own denouement.

"We got you, you Philistine."

"You got me."

Beth hugged him. "C'mon everyone," she said. "Into the kitchen."

The Big Raccoon whipped off his cap and mask. "Time to taste the fruits of our labor."

Adam's eyebrows arched. "Our labor?"

"Yours and mine. You grew it and I thrashed around in the dark picking it. That's not easy."

"But worth it for the laughs?"

"I suppose, but the laughs were an afterthought. You see, all that about the raccoons is true. I wanted to be sure you got your harvest."

Adam peered at him and, in that unguarded instant, recognized a genuine warmth in the depths of those pale blue eyes. Arm in arm, they followed the others out of the room.

"I guess I owe you my thanks. I hope the effort was worth it."

"Oh, yes. I made sure of that." He chuckled at the thought. "You're the only one who'd know the bag is two ears shy." ◇

Burying the Black Sheep

Catherine Wald

My cousin Oscar's funeral was a great disappointment.
It started promptly at eleven with no consideration for shifts
in alternate-side-of-the-street parking.

The vanilla eulogy that was served up
was most unsuited to a tutti-frutti schizophrenic
with a trenchant sense of humor
ironic attire
and a demeanor that alternated between angelic and criminal.

Due to a clerical error, the rabbi repeatedly referred to the grieving
      mother
by someone else's name.
After each *Doris*, the family members in the front three rows shouted
      back *Janet!*
in a spontaneous call-and-response that made
my crazy cousin's coffin wobble with laughter.

A younger rabbi took the mike and likened Oscar to a *tzaddik*—
one of thirty-six righteous men sent to live among us like embedded
    Zen masters.
He read from the Dead Sea Transcripts:
Stuyvesant High School,
president of the Jewish youth organization, Princeton
as if his life had ended already forty years ago.

My cousin's cohort almost nailed it when he described Oscar as a
luftmensch—a wind person, the Yiddish version of an airhead—
then followed up with a guitar-accompanied ballad about floating
    away in a cloud
that Oscar wrote back in the days when he was my hero.
The friend said a famous TV writer said,
All Oscar needs is a little success.
Which Oscar made sure he never got;
he believed in burning his bridges as soon as he got to them.

When it was over, I waited for some outraged Wald or Fruchtman
to leap up and fill in the blanks.
But no one did.
No one hissed:
He was mad, after all!
No one sneered:
We all admired him so much that his name was never mentioned
at family gatherings.
No one nudged:
He ripped out his mother's heart and fed it to the wolves three times a day.

Nor did anyone proffer the praise Oscar was really due
for making it all the way to sixty while living on the streets
busking for drug money
flushing his meds down the toilet
playing hide and seek with his muse
and hurtling insults at the vendors outside the temple
till the cops had to drag him away.

Worst of all, not a single ashen-faced woman tore her hair,
rent her mourning dress, or wailed
What will we do, now that our black sheep is gone? ◇

Poetry 101

Catherine Wald

Club me on the head
like a caveman or land me
a sucker punch to the gut.
Lay me low, green and foaming.

I wouldn't mind a slight damp tickle to the clit or
a wet whisper that raises the hairs on my inner ear.

Here's what I won't accept:

- Anything that doesn't excite or horrify
  me or make me feel I've just yanked open the refrigerator
  door barefoot, in a wet bathing suit.

- Wit (unless it's swift and cunning enough to
  stalk me through a dank alley, knock me upside the
  head, and run off with everything in my wallet).

- A stroll in a tidy English garden
  scented with violets (unless there is a wild-fanged wolf
  waiting in the bushes).

- A gondola ride down a Venetian canal
  (unless I can smell the urine-sweating stonework
  and see the bloated corpses rock
  to the rhythm of the tides).

- Fairy tales (unless they have poison
  or red-hot iron shoes for dancing).

I need to hear the witch's howls as she dies. ◇

At My Mother's Grave

Denise Mozilo Frasca

Somewhere in the deep
Recesses of my navel
There is genetic memory,
And sometimes it throbs at the loss.

Floating like an astronaut
Whose tether has come undone,
I long for gravity
Or, at least, a mother ship to guide me.

When my first was born
I studied her umbilical stump
So tender and angry, unfamiliar,
Searching for traces of myself.

Now both of us, healed,
Stand at your grave
Knowing, no matter,
The cord remains. ◇

Ode to a Road

Peter Wood

I HAVE FALLEN IN LOVE WITH A SMALL COUNTRY ROAD. EACH MORNING at six forty-five I hop into my car in Mount Kisco and head south into Armonk. Sometimes I turn on the radio, but I prefer listening to the poetry of Route 128. It is four and a half miles of beauty and eloquence: whispering evergreens, rumbling outcroppings, a burbling brook. I eavesdrop on the sighing hills, the murmuring meadows, and the singing apricot sky.

I don't want to get too sentimental about a country road. Freud might say, *Hey, sometimes a road is just a road.* But I know Thoreau would respond, *An unexamined road is not worth driving.* So every morning I examine this road. On my drive to school I ask small questions: Was this road once an Indian path? Who built those magnificent rock walls? How much do these homes cost?

As an adult I have learned to appreciate small things: my favorite spoon, a student's smile, this simple countryside road. Every morning my wife pours hot tea into my favorite blue cup and toasts me a bagel. Small things.

Small things are big things, I now realize, as I eat my breakfast, and they always have been. Try telling that to some of my high school students with their iPods, Ugg boots, and North Face jackets.

In my car every morning I play little games with myself. It's a tiny triumph when I guess the correct number of white swans swimming on Wampus Pond, or when I see a muskrat swimming in the water, or spot the same blackbird perched atop his favorite tree. Why does he choose *that* tree?

I never approach Route 128 without some trepidation. I remember a wild turkey that bolted from his flock and got clipped good. I clipped him. The long deep groove from his beak is still carved into my windshield. Farther south, by a row of golden sugar maples, I once saw an SUV swerve and narrowly miss a deer—but kill another. There's plenty of road kill on this road. I remember a buck as he stepped from the snow-covered pines one frozen December morning. He leaped over the metal guardrail and slipped onto his back on the icy pavement. Plumes of steam shot from his nostrils as he righted himself and nonchalantly trotted back into the woods. My right fender missed his hindquarter by inches. That deer was so much like me at eighteen, so much like some of my nonchalant sophomores—so clueless about death.

Last spring, driving toward Armonk, I saw a woman standing in the middle of the road talking to a rock. Actually, she was sobbing while bending over the rock. I stopped my car and stepped out. The rock had a head on it, feet, and a brown shell. It was a snapping turtle; its carapace had been cracked clear down the middle, and soft red meat oozed from beneath. I remembered another rock, forty-five years ago. My stepbrother was bending over it, holding his golf club. He was ten and I was eight. His rock had fur and a face and eyes. It was the bloody head of a kitten. He stood over it, laughing.

I hopped back into my car and drove to work. Sad memories of my unhappy family still breathe within my heart. Childhood isn't always over when it's over, is it? But driving down this Westchester road each day is a healing. There is power in its beauty and harmony. This road has always been a fine place to be alone, meditate, and calibrate myself.

On my morning drive, I dream. I'm now in the habit of recalling the good times and letting go of the bad, and I find simple spiritual strength in the greens, grays, and browns of the woods. In winter I notice I am able to peer deeper into the forest and spot things I normally wouldn't, like a vacant bird nest, wandering brooks, and winding trails. But there are other mornings when fog sets in and there's a heavy breathing in the morning darkness. Sometimes a moaning. Yes, if I'm not careful, the cold, pale dawn will suck the courage out of me and I will want to drive back home and climb back into bed.

Nevertheless, I have companionship on this road: squirrels, chipmunks, pheasants, turkeys, deer, ducks, muskrats, turtles, and swans. "Animals are different kinds of people than us, and rocks, too," said Dovie Thompson, a Lakota Indian poet visiting at my school. Someone else recently said, "Surround yourself with people better than you." I think that's exactly what I'm doing on Route 128.

Unfortunately, my tempestuous youth was never as harmonious as the morning pines and sunlit Norwegian spruce lining this road. Trees are nature's way of painting and on Route 128, color and diversity blend onto a quiet harmonious canvas. Why couldn't I, at eighteen, have paid closer attention? Are my students equally as blind to this beauty?

In the raucous hallways of my high school, where I teach, and in the dimly lit corridor of my memory, the pulse of the paint is still passion and youth. Mild madness darts about in adolescent confusion, and the hallways' heartbeat is a chaotic and colorful Basquiat mural. Students, now as then, are well behaved, except with each other. Even in my high school there is plenty of road kill in the hallways.

This morning, as I drove past Wampus Pond, I spotted that small muskrat swimming in the water. I was reminded of my older brother trapping muskrats in 1960 for their five-dollar pelts. This morning there were mallards on the pond and a flock of wild turkey grazing on the shore. A long pack of cyclists wearing redbluegreenyelloworange Spandex raced toward Mount Kisco. It's car traffic. Bike traffic. Animal traffic. Memory traffic. All of us are traveling the same road.

Driving home from school this afternoon, I looked out at the woods on Route 128. I drove past evergreens, rock walls, and the pond and I realized I'm still sitting in my classroom—I'm sitting in Room 128—and I'm *not* the teacher. I'm the *student*. My classroom for all these years has been the road, with the deer, the turtle, the muskrat, and the small blackbird perched atop his favorite tree. Their lessons and language are simple, wise, and beautiful. They are my blackboard and chalk. Small things. Beauty. I hope my students are listening. ◇

A Reunion

Gunter Nitsch

O N THE RAW, GRAY TUESDAY AFTERNOON OF DECEMBER 12, 1950, shortly after my thirteenth birthday, my father's new boss was driving my mother; my father; my eight-year-old brother, Hubert; and me through Cologne on the Rhine toward the town of Bergheim. The engine of Herr Meyer's overloaded Opel clattered and strained under the unaccustomed weight of its five passengers and all of our belongings. Except for the rickety taxi that had brought Mutti, Hubert, and me to the border during our escape from East Germany two years before, this was my first ride in any vehicle smaller than a Russian army truck.

A heavy carton packed with our two Bibles, my precious copies of *Huckleberry Finn* and *The Leatherstocking Tales,* my two atlases, and my stamp collection was crushing my lap. Hubert, who had barely managed to squeeze in between Mutti and me in the backseat, pressed against my side like an overstuffed piglet, breathing heavily. Having been force-fed a diet swimming in fat at a tuberculosis sanitarium, my brother was nearly as wide as he was tall. A few times I poked my elbow into his flabby side and whispered, "Give me some space, will you?" but he just glared at me, nervously brushing his straight blond hair away from his forehead.

Half an hour earlier our train had chugged slowly into the cavernous main railroad station, where my father, unsmiling, waited for us on the platform. This was our second reunion since the end of the war. Our first, in December of 1948, had ended abruptly with my father's announcement that he was leaving us to take a job as a pastry chef in Cologne. In the two years since he had abandoned us in a refugee camp near the East German border, my father had only intruded on our lives through infrequent postcards and even more infrequent transfers of funds. From my perspective, his abandonment had begun long before that. When I was a small child, he was away at war, rarely coming home on leave. Then, at war's end, while Mutti, Hubert, and I were trapped in Russian-held territory in the East, he had been captured by the British and had therefore lived in relative comfort in the West. Now this man, who was a virtual stranger to me, had sent us tickets so that we could join him.

My father introduced us to Herr Meyer moments after we stepped down from the train, and the five of us then walked outside together. Even though they were the same height, the two men could not have been more different. My father strode, stiff and fashionable, in his high-collared suit and heavy overcoat, his steel-gray eyes darting over the three of us anxiously. Herr Meyer slouched alongside us in a crumpled gray suit. In contrast to my father's bald head and gaunt frame, Herr Meyer had thick blond hair combed straight back, and his belt was nearly hidden below his protruding stomach. Laughter crinkled the corners of his blue eyes and he winked at Hubert and me as he struggled to fit our belongings into the tiny trunk of his car.

Sitting in the front passenger seat, my father stared straight ahead. Mutti, seated behind Herr Meyer, gazed glumly out the window as the car rumbled in the direction of Bergheim, twenty-four kilometers away. I couldn't see her face, but I was sure she and I were sharing the same thoughts. Had we just exchanged a hard life in the Bodenteich refugee camp for something even worse? At least in Bodenteich I could do pretty much as I pleased. I couldn't begin to imagine what it would take to please my father.

Wherever we looked, rubble left over from the allied bombing littered both sides of the road. The houses that were still standing were heavily pockmarked with bullet holes. Now and then we passed buildings where all the windows had been walled up with mismatched bricks scavenged from nearby ruins. Why would someone do that, I wondered. Were the owners trying to keep intruders out? Or were the bricked-up windows helping to keep the buildings from collapsing altogether? Had my father been a bit friendlier I would have asked him, but now I didn't dare.

Five long minutes passed without a word being spoken. Finally, Herr Meyer broke the silence.

"Well, Frau Nitsch," he said, trying to make eye contact with Mutti in the rearview mirror, "what are your first impressions of Cologne?"

"It reminds me of Königsberg," Mutti said slowly, "and Berlin. Terrible devastation everywhere you look."

"It's bad, that's for sure. But it's a paradise compared to the way the center of town looked in 1945. You know, around the main train station where we just were? Nearly everything over there was totally flat. It's a miracle the cathedral was spared."

My father suddenly turned to Herr Meyer and said bitterly, "Every time I come through this part of town, I get angry at the British and Americans for what they did here."

"What we did to the Russians wasn't any better," Mutti protested. "The stories the Russians told me about their civilian casualties would make your blood curdle. And don't forget that we started the war."

My father craned his neck around and glared at Mutti. "Now you listen to me! You'd better forget all that Communist propaganda and get on with your life or you'll never fit in here. Germany's different now. We've put all that behind us."

"Well, you may be angry at the British and the Americans," Herr Meyer said to my father, tactfully ignoring my parents' argument, "but the currency reforms they put through last year have really helped us get back on our feet."

"Well, I'll give them credit for that," my father said.

Mutti changed the subject. "I never thought to ask—which of the allies is in charge in this area?"

"Officially, it's a British zone," Herr Meyer replied. "But the troops stationed around here are from Belgium. I'll point out their barracks when we drive past Ichendorf."

We left Cologne, passing through the villages of Königsdorf and Horrem. Up to that point, we had been driving on a rather high plateau but now, straight ahead of us, lay a vast marshy plain divided into rectangular pastures, some enclosed by thick hedges, others bordered by ruler-straight rows of tall poplar trees. Never in my life had I been able to see so far. To our right, however, the plateau continued.

Herr Meyer nodded in that direction. "There's a big deposit of soft coal over there. See the smokestacks just behind the hills? Those are factories that produce briquettes and electricity."

"Is that how the houses are heated around here? With briquettes?" I asked timidly.

"That's pretty much all we use," Herr Meyer replied.

"Well then, at least I won't be chopping all that wood for the furnace," I said, thinking back to the backbreaking hours I had spent swinging an ax ever since I was barely eight years old.

"You'll have plenty of other chores to do, believe me," my father said sharply. "I'll see to that."

Holding tight to the box of books on my lap, I slumped down in my seat as far as my long legs would let me. Color had rushed into Mutti's cheeks. She reached across Hubert to place a reassuring hand on my arm. I could feel her hand trembling through my sleeve.

"Now, Willi," she said to my father, measuring every word, "Günter has been looking after us ever since Opa died back in 1946. You needn't worry about his carrying his own weight."

"Just so everyone knows who's in charge," my father said.

Mutti turned to me. With her free hand she pointed to herself and forced a smile.

Not long after that, we drove into a small town. "This is Bergheim," Herr Meyer announced, "and on your right, that's my café where we'll all have dinner later."

Mutti smiled gratefully and said, "That's very kind of you, Herr Meyer. We're certainly looking forward to it."

"Zieverich, where you'll be living, is just on the other side of the Aachener Tor, the old city gate ahead of us," Herr Meyer said.

The gate, with its two thick brick-and-mortar towers attached to an arched passageway, didn't look wide enough but Herr Meyer's Opel had no trouble passing through the narrow opening. As soon as we entered Zieverich we drove past a huge meadow on our right and a swamp on our left before crossing over the Erft River on a wide cement bridge. Just beyond the bridge, on the left, a driveway separated a Lutheran church from a tall building with two separate entrances. Herr Meyer made a U-turn on Aachener Strasse and parked in front of the entrance farther from the church.

"So, here you are," he said. "This is it."

A meter-high stone wall separated the front yards of the two attached parts of the house. The left half of the building had a fresh coat of plaster and large windows with crisp lace curtains and dark brown shutters. A front walk crossed a garden and led to a flight of steps going up to the door. But on the right side of the wall, six cement steps led down below the level of the sidewalk so that both the path and the first floor of the house on that side were well below street level. That half also had smaller windows. There were curtains but no shutters. And the front wall was still deeply pocked with bullet holes and shrapnel scars.

Herr Meyer opened the car door for Mutti and then went to the trunk to retrieve our things. Ignoring Hubert and me, my father joined him. I struggled desperately with the door on my side but couldn't open it. Herr Meyer, noticing my predicament, put our possessions on the sidewalk and came over to let Hubert and me out. "It's a little tricky," he said soothingly. Why couldn't my father be more like him, I wondered.

Herr Meyer shook hands with both of my parents. "It's so nice to see your family reunited at last," he said. "Now I've got to rush back to the shop. I'll see all of you in an hour for supper."

"Well," my father said as Herr Meyer drove off and we walked up to the front door, "we should let our landladies know we've arrived. At least one of the Lemm sisters should be home at this hour."

There were four doorbells. The bottom bell, with the nametag still blank, was ours. Next up was "Poltermann," then "van Knippenberg." The Lemm sisters' bell, which my father now pressed twice, was on top.

After a minute or two, we could hear the tapping of high-heeled shoes in the hallway and then a middle-aged lady opened the front door. Fräulein Lemm was wearing a long-sleeved, dark-blue, ankle-length dress. A cameo brooch held her collar tightly closed. Her hair was pulled back in a neat bun.

"Frau Nitsch and children, so glad to meet you!" she said, first shaking Mutti's hand and then mine and Hubert's. Her handshake reminded me of a limp dishrag. "I'm sorry that my sister isn't home to welcome you, too. Come in! Come in! No sense letting in the cold air and I'm sure you'd like to get settled."

We followed Fräulein Lemm into the wide entry hall and she stopped at the first door on the left. My father reached into his pocket for the key. "Please be sure to let me know if you need anything," Fräulein Lemm said, wringing her hands nervously. She suddenly seemed anxious to herd us all into the apartment.

Just then the door across the hall was flung open and out popped a tall skinny man with an enormous handlebar mustache and pitch-black stringy hair that hung at least five centimeters over his shirt collar.

"Well, here we go again!" he boomed. "More damn rrrefugees! As if we didn't have enough already!" He intentionally mispronounced the word "refugees" by imitating the rolling "r" of the East Prussian accent.

"Now listen here, Herr Poltermann," Fräulein Lemm started to say, but Herr Poltermann went right on.

"Don't take me too seriously," he said with a chuckle. "I can say whatever I like 'cause I'm a damn rrrefugee myself. Name's Poltermann. From Sudetenland. Just got back today from my in-laws' place in Fortuna."

"Nitsch," my father said, extending his hand.

"Well, well, well," Herr Poltermann replied, looking the four of us up and down. "A hearty welcome to Villa Lemm! So you'll be living down here with us *Untermenschen* on the ground floor. I'm sure Fräulein Lemm has told you how to find your way to the shithouse in the backyard. Refugees like us don't get indoor plumbing like the fancy-pants natives upstairs. Oh, no. We have to track way out back through the snow in the dead of night and sit there freezing our asses off in the dark while the wind whistles through the . . ."

"Please, Herr Poltermann, I beg you! You know very well that this is only a temporary solution," said Fräulein Lemm.

"Well, you're a nice one. What do you mean, temporary? My family has been living under these primitive conditions for a year now and there's no end in sight."

Fräulein Lemm turned to my parents, struggling to keep her composure. "Herr Poltermann has forgotten to say that as soon as my sister and I have the money we'll install a toilet in the first-floor laundry room."

"Don't make me laugh!" Herr Poltermann said sharply. Then he grinned at us. "You'll see soon enough who's right! *Aufwiedersehen!*" And he ducked back inside his apartment.

Fräulein Lemm sighed. "A very difficult gentleman," she said. "As I'm sure your husband has told you," she added, smiling weakly at Mutti, "the van Knippenberg family lives on the second floor and my sister and I live on the third floor. The van Knippenbergs are an old established family in this area, very refined people. They have three daughters. They lost their only son in a bombing raid in 1944. He was only fourteen, the poor dear." Fräulein Lemm barely paused to take a breath. "Herr van Knippenberg is the principal of the Catholic school here in Zieverich. I presume your boys will be attending there."

"The boys will go to the Lutheran school in Bergheim," my father interjected.

"That's too bad," Fräulein Lemm said. "It's two kilometers each way, and a few days a week they'll have to go back and forth twice, when the school has morning and afternoon shifts."

"I'm sure the walk will do them good," my father said. I tried to imagine my fat little brother walking eight kilometers a day. That's easy for him to say, I thought to myself.

"But at least you won't have far to go to get to church," Fräulein Lemm hastened to add. "It's right next door. Pastor Kampe and his family live in the other half of this building, by the way. Oh, and I almost forgot. We all use the other room on this side for doing laundry.

You'll find the entrance back there by the staircase."

"Thank you so much for the information, and good evening, Fräulein Lemm," my father said.

Fräulein Lemm nodded, smiled, and walked farther down the hallway to the wooden stairs leading up to the apartment she shared with her sister. When she was out of earshot, Mutti asked my father, "Is that customary here to have such long conversations in the hallway?"

"There wouldn't have been space for all five of us to talk inside," my father replied as he finally turned the key in the lock and we got our first look at our new home.

I let out a low whistle. "It's not much bigger than our room in the refugee camp in Bodenteich!" I would have said more but the angry look my father shot me kept me quiet.

To our right a row of clothes hooks was attached to a thick wooden board nailed to the wall. A double bed took up all of the remaining space on that side. A sink and stove were to the left of the doorway. On the far left side of the room, a single window faced the front yard and, next to it, a couch, a rectangular table, and two stools completed the furnishings.

"I see what you mean," Mutti said. "There's barely enough space in here for the four of us. Where will the boys sleep?"

"Hubert can sleep on the couch and Herr Meyer gave me an old military folding cot that Günter can use. It slides right under the couch. We'll have to set it up every night, that's all."

"Where?" Mutti protested, eying the narrow area between the table and the double bed.

"Oh, it'll fit all right. When the boys go to bed, we'll just have to move the table and chairs over there." He pointed to the cramped space in front of the coat hooks.

I looked up at the single ceiling light over the spot where my cot would be. I took a deep breath and said to my father, "Could I ask you something? When I go to bed, will that light still be on?"

"Of course it will," my father snapped. "Do you think your mother and I are going to spend our evenings in the dark?"

"Don't be so hard on Günter," Mutti protested. "He has the right to ask a simple question."

"Now you listen to me, all of you," my father ordered. "There's a severe housing shortage around here and we'll just have to make the best of what we have."

Without another word, Mutti unpacked a towel from her bag and we all washed our hands over the kitchen sink before setting out for Café Meyer.

In silence the four of us left the house, climbed the cement steps up to the sidewalk, and turned to the right in the direction of Bergheim. By 1950 my parents had been married for fifteen years but they'd only actually lived together for less than four. Although they now walked side by side, my father kept his hands firmly in his coat pockets. He and my mother never so much as glanced at each other. As Hubert and I dawdled along behind them I tried my hardest to imagine how differently they must have acted as newlyweds in the years before the war. Living here isn't going to be easy for Hubert and me, I decided, but how much worse must it be for Mutti!

After crossing over the river and passing the meadow and the swamp, we walked through the pedestrian passageway on the right side of the Aachener Tor. Just past the Freiburg clothing shop and the Stüssgen Food Market we reached the café. The sign on the door said "Closed" but the lights were blazing inside. Herr Meyer was waiting to greet us, together with a tall, ash-blond lady with a charming smile and big dimples.

"Allow me to introduce you to my wife," Herr Meyer said. "Dear, this is Herr Nitsch's wife and these are his two boys, Günter and Hubert."

"So nice to meet you, Frau Meyer," Mutti said shyly, trying her best to smile. "I must apologize for how the boys and I are dressed. We didn't have time to change."

"There's no need to apologize!" Frau Meyer exclaimed, her eyes sparkling. "We're just happy to welcome you to Bergheim! Josef and I have lived here all our lives and we really love this place. Once you get settled in, I'm sure you will, too. But let's not waste time on small talk. You must all be starving after your long trip. Excuse me just a minute." She turned and shouted toward the back of the shop, "Maria, our guests are here!"

Frau Meyer led us past several small marble-top tables to a larger table set for six. Atop an embroidered white-linen tablecloth were six heavy porcelain plates decorated with blue and white painted wildflowers. Each of us had been provided with a soupspoon, a teaspoon, a dinner fork, a dessert fork, and a knife. I couldn't imagine how any one person could use so much silverware. Throughout the meal I carefully observed my parents and Herr and Frau Meyer to be sure that I was using the right utensil at the right time.

Since, for the past two years, my supper had been limited to two slices of rye bread spread with lard and onions and one slice of bread with sugar-beet syrup, I was totally unprepared for the meal that followed. We started with a thick vegetable soup, followed by sauerbraten with red cabbage, and mashed potatoes soaked with real butter. Ignoring the grown-ups' small talk, I proceeded to stuff myself, barely stopping long enough to breathe. When I was just about ready to burst, Maria brought out the dessert, together with real coffee for the adults and hot chocolate for Hubert and me.

Herr Meyer beamed. "Boys, I want you to know that the tart was made by your father. Isn't it beautiful? And I'll tell you a secret. It tastes even better than it looks."

The fruit tart really was a work of art. Peach slices circled the outer edge. Semicircles of a pale yellow fruit nestled between the peaches and four banana halves. And, in the center, a whole ring of the mysterious pale fruit was garnished with bright-red cherries.

"I recognize the bananas, peaches, and cherries, but what's the other fruit?" I asked, looking from my father to Herr Meyer.

Herr Meyer smiled. "That's canned Dole pineapple, imported from Hawaii. It's a bit expensive, but I think you'll find that it's well worth it."

I put a big dollop of whipped cream on the slice of tart Maria served me and ate very slowly, savoring every bite. Hubert finished his piece first and we were both relieved when Frau Meyer insisted that he and I have seconds. Maria also brought Hubert and me another cup of hot chocolate, but instead of more coffee for the adults she brought out four crystal glasses and a bottle of wine.

"How about a little Kröver Nacktarsch to cap off the evening?" Herr Meyer said. He held up the bottle so that we could all see the picture on the label of a little boy, his short pants pulled down to the top of his knee socks, getting spanked on his bare bottom by a vintner. My father burst out laughing.

Even Mutti started to giggle. "I can't remember when I last tasted wine but I've never seen a bottle like that," she admitted.

"It's one of our favorite Mosels," Herr Meyer said. "Guaranteed to liven up any occasion." Then he winked at Hubert and me. "Sorry, boys, but as you can see, this stuff's off-limits for children!"

By the time the adults had finished a second bottle of wine, they were chatting away like old friends.

"So how does your new place compare with where you were before?" Herr Meyer suddenly asked Mutti. "Pretty cramped space for four people, I'd say."

"Now, Josef," his wife began, but Herr Meyer went right on.

"If you can keep this under your hats," he said, leaning across the table and grabbing my father's sleeve, "when I ran into Fräulein Lemm a few days ago in the butcher shop she hinted that she was trying to get the Poltermanns out so that your family could have two additional rooms."

"I wouldn't mind that," Mutti chimed in. "I couldn't believe how insulting Herr Poltermann was to Fräulein Lemm this afternoon."

"That's just his sense of humor," my father said. "He's perfectly harmless."

"Well, I wouldn't put up with it," Mutti replied firmly.

"Actually, he's got the law on his side," my father explained. "The way I understand it, once someone rents space to refugees, it's pretty hard to evict them."

"All the same, I'll let you know if I hear anything more about it," Herr Meyer added as he leaned back in his chair with a conspiratorial grin.

MUTTI WAS A LITTLE WOBBLY on the walk back to Zieverich and, almost without thinking, she grabbed my father's arm to steady herself. The

Kröver Nacktarsch and the fine meal had certainly worked wonders. By the time we got back to our room, all four of us were talking at once.

My father held up his hand to get our attention. "Now, let's see how fast I can put Günter's cot together," he said, as he carried the small rectangular table and the two stools to the opposite corner by the door. Then, reaching down, he dragged a bulky olive-green canvas pack out from under the couch as Hubert, Mutti, and I sat down to watch.

"I had lots of practice with these when I worked in the military hospital in Berlin," he said to me, "but it took me a while to get the hang of it. I want you to watch what I'm doing so that you can make up the cot yourself." Within minutes he had unfolded the canvas cot on its three pairs of crossed wooden legs. Mutti put a folded blanket and a sheet on top. It was the first time in my life I could remember seeing my parents working together as a team.

"Give it a try," my father encouraged me. "I hope it's long enough. Just be careful not to get pinched by the frame."

The cot was surprisingly comfortable except for the sharp edges of the six square wooden pegs connecting the legs to the sides. And it was even better when Mutti added my pillow and the lumpy feather comforter I'd brought from the refugee camp. After Hubert and I had washed up and brushed our teeth over the sink, Mutti asked us to close our eyes so that she and my father could undress for bed.

My parents had bickered from the Cologne railroad station until we got to Café Meyer. Our room was a bit cramped and the idea of living with my father was something I'd have to get used to. But my father had softened as the evening wore on. Maybe things won't be so bad after all, I thought, and then I fell asleep before my parents turned off the light. ◇

Commute

Elizabeth Meaney

It's too early for this Salvador Dali skyline,
New York melting at eight fifty-eight,
Oiled skyscrapers slicking sweat on my scalp.
This is my gear-grinded commute,
Crushed between iron tracks, filed by
Two strangers' irritations, their poly-blend clothes.
I've only a cufflink-slit, a narrow moment where
I swipe my card, to exhale the second it beeps.
Below ground, our collective breaths gather
Like ghosts, haunt incessantly the train cars,
Avoiding the cracked grime of the windows,
Unwilling to escape.
How I wish instead, I'd sent myself
Someplace sun-still and distant in an envelope
Of clean, white sheets.
The sweat of that man pushes itself on me
Like a persistent salesman.
The pole is slicked from an anonymous palm.
When the doors half-open, we squeeze through
Like an asthmatic cough.

Then the work day begins. ◇

Unmade Bed

Elizabeth Meaney

Alone all day, our bed waits for us,
rustling its sheets, confessing secrets to the walls.
It plots to lure us back—
trap us, tug us with terry-cloth ties,
send us rolled in sheets by FedEx, faster home—
but sighs and admits it's too lazy
to lift itself from its frame.

Like an abandoned scene
where waking up called us to the witness stand,
our conspiracy appears interrupted,
twisted sheets disclosing dents in the pillow,
quilt bunched untouched
in one corner, excluded from the sunk center
where your hardest parts find my softest. This is a
place of bare feet, cracked heels, and the
intimacy of our dropped voices
that makes most important
the shape of our lips, our peeking tongues.

I feel unshelled all day,
a snail unarmed; a hermit crab between homes.
My spine shoots vain sparks to signal your stomach
to reconvene within peeling paint-cracks, the corners
where our noses meet up to admit
they've missed each other's smells. ◇

The World in Me

Kristina Bicher

I did not make the sky
make it blue
make blue—
these are not my trees
snapping shaggy limbs
into a gust that strings
clouds along the sky

The world sprung
me into it
yet this very day
moves in me like breath
as if it were my own
as if I am made
for just this ◇

A Short Riff on Sixty-fifth

Stanley Sokol

M Y FIRST THOUGHT AS I SIT DOWN OUTSIDE OF FERRIER'S, ON
East Sixty-fifth Street, is that the graybeard at the next table
has his hands full trying to give advice to his daughter. It's an
understandable mistake, since he's much older, and any father with a
daughter so beautiful would be very worried. But I only need to hear a
little of their conversation to realize his difficulties are more romantic
than paternal.

"Why? Am I too old?" he asks her.

"No," she says, and she mashes her sexy lips and delightful little
nose with the back of her hand, as if she's thinking about his fate. She
takes her hand away and moves it across the table as if waving him off.
The sight of her lipstick-stained fingers sends a tingle down my spine
as I hear her say to him, "But you're too predictable."

Now he's the one thinking, and although the spa-tanned faces of
everyone seated at these tables are flashing "limousine," I'm hoping
this guy recently took a ride on the Lexington Avenue subway, where
he might have seen, posted in almost every train, that poem about
a woman who is *so beautiful that she or time must fade*. And what I'm
feeling is, that's what he should say to her.

Instead he starts singing softly, "For it's a long, long time from May

125

to December, And the days grow short when you reach —"

I don't blame her when she cuts him off by raising her hand, and says, "You're always singing old songs."

He says, "Well what am I going to sing? I certainly can't understand the rappers."

"How about Celine Dion? She's not a rapper and anyone can understand her."

"She has a sort of insipid quality to her voice, don't you think?"

Now her nose and mouth are crinkled so her face is getting to look like she ate something that should have been thrown away. And he sees what I'm seeing and he is not happy.

She says, "Insipid? You probably think there hasn't been a decent female vocalist since Billie Holiday."

"Well, she set a standard that's hard to match."

"Bullshit. Billie Holiday never learned to sing in tune."

"Ella Fitzgerald?" he asks.

She answers him with a jerk of her foxy little head, turning so she's facing me, and when she sees that I've been listening, she arches her eyebrows and pulls her head back, a gesture I take as meaning *hmm*. Then she slowly turns back toward him and says, "You know, I was wrong. It's not that you're predictable; it's just that you're too old."

She gets up and heads down the street with a walk that makes me feel twenty years younger. I see this sad old fart watching her insouciant ass disappear from his life, and it comes to me that, though she's wrong about Billie Holiday, the point here is that sometimes beauty has to take priority over truth.

Two days later, I'm sitting in the same seat at the same table, cultivating my memories, and a cab pulls up and out pops this same foxy chick. Only this time, instead of the standard East Side white summer outfit from Prada, what she's wearing, held up by two spaghetti straps, is one of those almost-dresses that go from distinctly above the knees to just below her cleavage. And while I'm noticing that she's even sexier than I remember, and I'm reflecting on how I would like to have been one of the three people it took to get her into that dress, her escort gets out of the cab.

He's this big black dude, and he's wearing what they used to call a Super Fly outfit. He's got on a cream suit, with a collarless black shirt buttoned at the neck, and a white homburg set so the brim covers one eyebrow. In case that's not enough over the top, he's also got a white ivory cross hanging from a gold chain around his neck. In other words, he looks like a refugee from the Buena Vista Social Club.

They sit down at the next table and he waves to the waiter, saying, "Over here, my man. We wish to place our order."

Now the thing I love about Manhattan is that everybody is trying hard to not look at this couple, pretending this twosome is just run-of-the-mill, everyday Big Apple baloney. Of course, they're all sneaking looks because this is too good a story not to be enjoyed and retold to get an evening's party from cocktails to dinner.

After he orders two margaritas, the guy says, "So you finally got rid of Wrinkles?"

She says, "Yeah, he kept pushing Kurt Weill at me. How many times can you hear 'September Song'?"

"Yeah," he says. "I know what you mean—no class. Andrew Marvell would have been a cooler choice."

"Perhaps," she says.

He starts reciting, "*Had we but world enough, and time, This coyness, baby, were no crime.*"

I just can't help myself; I laugh out loud. And he looks at me, angry, and says, "Excuse me, what the fuck are you laughing about?" And while he's doing his best to look big and mean, I know from the "excuse me" that he's probably not a hard case.

So I say to him, "I didn't mean any disrespect. I laughed because *baby* is so out of place in the poem. The word is *Lady*, with a capital L."

"That doesn't make sense," he says. "The poet is talking to his coy mistress, who he's trying to get into bed; baby makes more sense."

"Andrew Marvell wrote this three or four hundred years ago," I say. "They didn't use the word *baby* the way we do today."

I glance at Miss Foxy then—a mistake—because he sees me grab the look, and now our disagreement becomes a contest.

"How the fuck do you know?" he says, and looks me up and down.

"You don't look like no professor to me."

"Well," I say, looking him up and down, "you sure as shit don't look like any kind of professor either."

He says, "What are you trying to say?" and he puts his hands on the arms of his chair as if he's about to stand. But I've got this guy figured for bluff and bluster because, by now, a heavyweight would have either turned his back to me or flattened my ass.

He goes on, "Are you trying to say that a black man in a white suit can't know Andrew Marvell's poetry?"

"Listen," I say, "meaning no disrespect to you or your lady," and here I nod to Miss Foxy and I take full notice of her nodding back, "no disrespect, but Marvell wrote *lady*, not *baby*."

Then comes an inspiration and while I know it's not true, I tell him, "I would never say a black man doesn't know Marvell's poetry, because Marvell himself was black."

He looks at me skeptically. "Don't be jiving me," he says. "You just told me this was written more than three hundred years ago."

This guy has a point. I need to give him someone famous from long ago with a dark complexion. I tell him, "So? Shakespeare wrote about Othello, the Moor, before Marvell was born. And that's what you are—a Moor."

He presses his lips together and nods, as if the idea appeals to him, so he turns to Miss Foxy and says, "How do you like being cast as Desdemona?"

"I don't," she says. "I'm not interested in being anyone's victim."

"Then who would you like to be cast as—Lady Macbeth?"

A double mistake, I think: first, because it attacks her, and second, because it shows a lack of imagination.

"It would be nice," she says, "if you could think of me as Beatrice."

He nervously adjusts his big white hat and says, "I never could get into Dante."

"Not Dante's Beatrice," she says. "Shakespeare's—from *Much Ado About Nothing*."

"Yeah," he says, "I saw that movie—for sure she's more than a handful."

Miss Foxy does some pouting about this remark, so I step in.

"How about Isabel Archer," I say.

"Another victim," Miss Foxy says, and Othello gives me a smug smile like "Hah, she's skewered you, too."

"Maybe not," I say. "It's possible that Henry James meant she was free to make mistakes—just like any man."

She smiles at this explanation and when Othello sees that, he says, "Let's get out of here." Then he looks at me. "Too many old folks."

As she leaves with him, she looks me up and down as if commenting on what I'm wearing. I'm thinking she's thinking that my attempt at East Side rags is not much better than his New York Super Fly extravagance. I look at my funky sport jacket that the snotty salesman at Barney's talked me into buying, and my baggy beige pants, and I think this will never do—this is not my stuff.

So I figure I'll give it a try, and I turn up at Ferrier's every day for six days in a row, and after careful consideration, I alternate wearing my soft-brown summer suit with the soft-blue one. I'm wearing a freshly laundered white shirt—a new one would look better, but a new shirt every day smacks of excess, and even if others might not know it's new, I would. And I have on a matching tie from the handful of Italian silk ones I bought in London last winter. Instead of the Dos Equis I've been drinking, I order a dry martini with a small celery stalk in lieu of the expected olive.

On the second day the waiter, who has noticed everything, says, as he brings my martini, "She ain't coming back."

"I'm giving it my best shot," I answer, and that day I start leaving him an extra large tip for good luck and also as a reward for his taking a role in this little drama.

On the sixth day, which is the best June day so far, she shows up in one of those summer dresses Irwin Shaw wrote about, the kind that clings to a woman's body and uses the breeze to play with her curves. A dress showing enough to make a man feel the song in his testicles that Hemingway described, but not so much that he's reduced to the mindless slobbering of a Portnoy.

She sits down at my table and when the waiter comes, she says, "I'll have the same," and points to my drink.

I say, "You look just right."

"How do you mean?"

"The other two outfits I've seen you in were not you, in Manhattan, in June; this one is."

"You look just right also," she says.

"How do you mean?" I ask.

"More age-appropriate," she says, "not excessive, but an attractive background for me."

At this point, the waiter comes back, gives us each a martini with a celery stalk and says, "This is on me."

"Why?" she says.

"Why not?" the waiter says, taking my empty glass, and our secret, away with him.

"So what happened to Wrinkles and Othello?" I say. "Is it all over with them?"

"Yes, yes," she sighs. "And what's your name?"

"Woids."

"Words?"

"No. Woids—with an i."

"Oh, Woids." She laughs. "I like it. You know, you're not a bad-looking guy and you're amusing and you seem to want to be with me, but why? What is it about me?"

I realize it's a full count: I'm at bat and she's thrown me a curveball and I could foul it off and stall, but my gut tells me to swing for the fences. So I say, "You're the woman Richard Wilbur is talking about in the poem they plastered all over the subways last winter."

"I never ride the subway," she says.

"It's a very interesting place," I say, "with things like this poem about this woman who is, quote, *So beautiful that she or time must fade*. This poet also does Andrew Marvell one better. Where Marvell wants his coy mistress to forget her looks and help him make the sun run, the subway poet talks about a woman whose presence can confuse the sun so that it forgets to run."

"Well, Woids, you overwhelm me," she says. "Is it your plan for us to stop time?"

"No. Richard Wilbur finishes the poem by saying nothing happens except her walk down the street, quote, *Leaving the stations of her body there / Like whips that map the countries of the air.*"

She asks, "'Countries of the air'? What does that mean?"

"I think it's about making an indelible impression on time."

"Indelible?"

"Well, at least a mark that we were here."

"Sounds like we're back to Marvell," she says, and now I'm totally smitten.

I see that we're moving in the right direction, so I say, "Why don't we take a stroll somewhere and get to know each other?"

I get up, throw some money on the table, and hold out my hand for her. She stands and gives me her hand and I tuck it under my arm.

"Where shall we go?" she asks.

"First," I say, "let's take Edward Lear's advice and find a place where we can dance *by the light of the moon, the moon,* and we'll dance by the light of the moon."

Her smile says that she finds this prospect very pleasant, and easy to entertain.

"And then," she asks, "what will we do second?"

I say, "We'll go off *to sea in a beautiful pea-green boat.* And we'll take *some money and plenty of honey, wrapped up in a five-pound note.*"

"Sounds delightful," she says.

And we take off into the cool Manhattan summer evening. For the first time in my life, I sense that truth and beauty have been woven together into the feeling of toploftiness Scott Fitzgerald wrote about when he was here, so many years ago. And I tell her what I'm feeling.

She says, "It's hard to maintain that kind of feeling for more than a little while." Then, with a sly smile, she adds, "Feelings can be as fleeting as the countries of the air."

Hearing her say that, I feel Manhattan miss a beat. For an instant, nothing moves. Was I about to go the same way as Wrinkles and Othello? Or was she, like Billie Holiday, only pausing at some surprising place in the lyrics? Then, just the way Billie, on her old records, would pick it up, and Teddy Wilson and Benny Goodman would come in doodling behind her, the beat of the city comes back, and we walk on, with Manhattan bopping behind us. ◇

When I Hear His Voice

Lee Eiferman

A THOUSAND LITTLE THINGS HAVE TO GO EXACTLY RIGHT IN ORDER for my dad to say it's okay for us to work the farmers market. The electric line to the house can't quit or else my alarm won't ring. The gas station with the cheap gas has to open at 4:30—that's a.m. And A-Number-One: a fine-looking crop of flowers and herbs in the spring, and enough tomatoes, radishes, and squash in the fall have to be ready to go in order to balance out the expense and "headache" (as my dad calls it) of traveling to the city and back again.

We used to do berries, too, but my dad says they're too labor-intensive. I love blueberries. I loved picking them. But I'm not an ideal picker. There's a trick to knowing when you should empty the berries into a collection tin. It's just like how they describe it in *Blueberries for Sal*. The little bear follows little Sal up the mountain, grabbing handfuls of Sal's picked blueberries as they fall, PLONK! PLONK! into the can. When I was little and my mama was still alive, she used to read that book to me again and again. Could be that's why I loved to go picking. Then last spring my dad announced we were no longer in the berry business and plowed half the plants under. I suppose too many dribbled out of my hands when I picked them. I could feel that happening.

My sister knows I have a thing for this guy at the market, so before we pull into our assigned parking spot, she checks my lipstick line. My hands shake a bit. I suppose it's nerves. When I hear his voice I get this fluttery feeling in the back of my throat. It's a deep voice with a round sweetness about it, like he was raised by someone who took the time to make him French toast with real maple syrup. Once, while we were packing up at the end of the day, his hand brushed against mine. He didn't pull back like my hand was a hot oven. Instead he just apologized with that sweet and deep voice, and my stomach commenced to doing flip-flops.

I know it's crazy. He probably has a fine wife and three kids, all with sweet voices just like his. Once, after lunch and before the evening rush, on a Tuesday afternoon, we talked about music. He likes rap and hip-hop, which are not the same thing, he told me. I love *High School Musical*. He couldn't get over that and laughed. His laugh didn't sound mean, but more like a "you're killing me" chuckle. I traded some daffodils for his organic lamb. My dad said the lamb tasted mighty clean but that it was too expensive so I couldn't trade with him anymore.

That's kind of sad, because now I'm thinking how all those people that buy his lamb and goat cheese are suckers. My sister told me his hair is red. People always do that, they tell me the color of things as if that's supposed to mean something to me.

Sometimes it does. Like red is the feeling of the plastic tablecloth frying and cracking in the noonday sun.

And blue is the pond at the base of the sloping field that cools my hand after it's touched the red tablecloth. ◇

Duck Pond in Tuckahoe

Adrienne Hernandez

He sits on a bench dedicated
to someone's beloved wife
(perhaps his own)
as ducks swim in pairs
geese squawk
a commuter train roars
like a wounded elk
and birds become bats
as night falls.

The black Lab at his feet
knows the futility of waiting
but keeps this to himself. ◇

God of Potential Things

Rosetta Benson

Who but such a god would deign to read
the soul of scales, scraped clean of fish,
no longer bound to skin or shape,
appreciate their aptitude to dry and flake
and curve much like a sail
having at last freedom to fly
and give them wind? ◇

Ms. Murphy's Makeover

Jacqueline Grandsire Goldstein

IT WAS ALMOST CHRISTMAS VACATION, AND ME, MONROE, AND Suzette were in charge of a gift from the cosmetology class to our English teacher, Ms. Murphy. It's like a promotion the school has—a *Morning of Beauty*. We usually charge for it, but for Murphy it was on the house. I got the idea of the makeover from watching cable—a show called *What Not to Wear*. Murphy really needs to get on that show, but this is the next best thing. We came in before the start of regular classes, even Monroe, who usually makes it to school around ten. We were all in the Christmas spirit.

Murphy goes and sits in one of the chairs with the old-fashioned helmet hair dryer over it. It's almost like she's trying to hide. But Suzette pulls her out from there and over to the sink.

"Try to relax, Miss," I tell Murphy. She is gripping the arms of the green chair. "You're too tense."

Wordplay. It's good for the kids. Helps them manipulate language.

"Teepee, wigwam," Murphy says.

"Excuse me, Miss?"

"Teepee, wigwam. Two tents. Too tense. You told me I was too tense. Get it?"

She is a little corny. It's part of her job.

"Just a joke," she says. "An English teacher joke." While Suzette puts the cape over Murphy, I get to check her out up close. She has that freckled skin that gets old fast and needs extra moisturizer. I won't use the stuff in the cabinets. Nothing behind those glass doors has seen the light of day in at least twenty years. But there's a secret stash of samples in Collins's closet.

At least Murphy has good nails. "Miss, your nails are beautiful," I tell her. Her nails are strong, and with real half-moons. "It makes the job so easy when you have good material to work with," I say. And Murphy's mouth turns up a little, making lines in the cream I just put on her face.

"I know what you mean. *You* did well on your essay, Valerie," she tells me. "As usual." Yeah, I get it. Murphy loves me. All my teachers do. I hope she doesn't start in about college again.

"How did *I* do?" asks Suzette. Suzette is about to start washing Murphy's hair. She turns on the faucets and starts testing the water. It comes out brown at first so you have to let it run. I can see Murphy getting nervous and I don't blame her, being that Suzette is failing English.

"I didn't get to yours yet," Murphy tells Suzette.

"Why can't you teachers tell the truth? That means I failed," says Suzette. "*As usual.*" There are tears in Suzette's eyes. I swear. Murphy looks really nervous now.

Suzette says, "It's all good, Miss. I wouldn't take it out on your hair."

Like hell she wouldn't.

"Be easy, Miss Murphy," Suzette says. Suzette starts the final rinse and then wraps Murphy's hair in a black towel. Murphy is pretty and all, but with the towel you can see that she wouldn't look so good in black hair. You need to go lighter as you get older and Murphy is at least thirty-five. She has twins who are in high school.

While I take Murphy over to the haircutting station, Suzette is studying on an old *Hairstyles* magazine we keep on this rack we have.

I get Murphy settled in the styling chair and get rid of the towel. Murphy's hair combs out no problem. Still, she has a lot of split ends from pulling her hair back with rubber bands and twisting it into a pony tail. We keep telling her that it damages the hair but she doesn't listen.

Suzette just tears out the page from the magazine and sticks it up on the mirror with some tape. Then she starts to cut, and pretty soon there's a lot of red hair on the green linoleum floor. I can see already that Murphy is gonna look great. Monroe sweeps up the hair and gets ready to do his thing.

Monroe never shows up for tests in the regular subjects so there's no question about how he did on the essay. But he is the best with the leg massage.

Now Monroe starts filling up the little portable pedicure tub, and don't worry—it's clean because I took care of that myself.

Excruciating. Good vocabulary word for the kids. Use in a sentence. It is excruciating to be poked and prodded by the students in your English class. Excruciating.

"Excruciating."

"What's that word, Miss?" I ask her.

"Never mind. Those are good posters," Murphy says, looking at our charts.

"Thank you, Miss," I say. "I did the one on pincurls."

"Pincurls?"

"Yeah, we have to do them for the state licensing test. You know, the practical."

Anyway I take off her loafers and her little knee-high stockings and put them down on the floor real neat so she can see them but nobody will trip over them. She's looking down at Monroe's dreadlocks. He's bending over her feet and even though he's pressing his thumbs into her arches where there is a sweet spot, I don't think she's having a good time.

"You have great cuticles," I tell Murphy. "Do you want a design? I can do a snowflake. Or even Santa Claus. I've been practicing."

"NO!" Murphy says, real loud. I didn't know she could get that loud.

"No snowflake," Murphy says in her regular voice. "No design. And don't you have a lighter color? Maybe just some clear polish?"

I bought the cranberry polish myself at CVS. The school just has this cheap old junk and I'm not using that on her.

"Color," I tell her. "Otherwise the class will say I cheated them."

I start to rub cream into her hands. "Make her take her rings off," Suzette says. "The cream is getting them all dull."

Murphy looks down at her hands. "Is that necessary?"

"No, Miss," I answer. "But it would be better."

She waits another beat, and then starts tugging them off. I bet they've never been off her finger since she said I do. She probably keeps them on even when she does dishes. That's why there's this red dent on her finger. And she's done plenty of dishes, I can tell. So she puts the rings in her purse and holds out her hand again to me and knocks the bag over. Some stuff falls out: her wallet and like twenty pens and some papers. When I pick it up for her I see an envelope from R. Gordon, Attorney at Law. So—Murphy has a lawyer. I guess we know about lawyers here in the Bronx. But that is strictly NOMB—none of my business.

Anyway, after she puts her stuff back in her bag she seems kind of shaky. I make sure the purse stays in her lap. I mean, none of us would rob Murphy, but this is the Bronx. I could just see those diamonds sparkling in somebody's teeth. That is one stubborn little red dent where the rings had been.

"You should take those rings off when you do the dishes, Miss," I tell her. "You get soap under it. Your finger needs fresh air once in a while."

She doesn't say anything, so I keep talking.

"Just relax, Miss," I say. "Breathe. Make believe you don't know us. We're professionals. We do this every day. Close your eyes and pretend you're on a beach or something."

"NO BEACH!" she says real loud.

Now that's funny, because she used to show us pictures of her and her husband at this beach in California. She has a picture on her desk of him and the twins at the beach, too. He is mad good-looking. His name is Francis, she told us. Not Frank or Frankie. Francis. Not a lot of teachers will tell you stuff like that.

I keep working on her polish. I give her the snowflake on her pinky and she doesn't say anything so I keep going on the rest of her nails. "Didn't you say you were going to California for Christmas? With Mr. Murphy?" Maybe I shouldn't ask but I'm kind of curious.

"Plans have changed," she tells me. She closes her eyes, like she's really tired.

A beach. Of all places. Why did Valerie have to say beach? Behind her closed eyes, unbidden, the scene replays.

Francis had been in the shower and his laptop was still open on the dresser. She never knew what sudden impulse made her pass her hand over the screen saver. A photograph appeared beneath her hand. Francis was standing bare-chested behind a woman in a black swimsuit. The woman was tanned a uniform caramel color, contrasting with Francis's reddened skin. His head was resting on top of hers, and his arms were wrapped tightly around hers in an X, grazing her breasts.

Murphy still looks tense, but the cream Monroe is using smells like peaches, and that should calm her down. He's working her calves, rotating her ankles. He moves her toes back and forth. He's massaging heavy cream into them, rubbing it in and around her toes like they taught us. She probably never even had a pedicure before. You can tell she's embarrassed, but Monroe just keeps working it in, and of course he's strictly cool about it. With his black nail polish, done by me, he looks great. I could imagine him one day as a stylist to the stars, if he ever gets it together. But I guess it's tough for Murphy, having a student rub her legs, and a guy student at that. But wait. I think she's getting into it. Murphy lets out this big sigh. "That's it, Miss. Let it all out. Teepee whatever," I say.

"Wigwam," she says. "A Native American home."

141

I start the polish on her toes. "That's right, Miss. Just hold still." She's not even looking. It's like she's miles away. That's good. So I give her the snowflakes there, too, and she doesn't say anything and I start talking about the SATs. I took them because Murphy was on my case about it so much and with the fee waiver we get, it doesn't cost anything. They were mad hard. "But those vocabulary words you give us helped me," I tell Murphy. "They were all on there." She's like drifting off. I finish her toes and start putting on the foundation and blush. When she closes her eyes I take my chance to do the eye shadow.

"The SATs. If we do this right now it will mess up the girls," Francis had said. "SATs. College applications. All that stuff. No need to decide anything now."

"Why wasn't I enough?" she asked over and over

His face was still sunburned from his little side trip in California. "I told you a dozen times already. It's nothing. She means nothing."

She had pulled her rings off then, left them on the kitchen table in front of her husband. "This doesn't have to change anything," he continued. "You're still my wife. The mother of my children. You know I'd give my right arm for you—for you and for . . . ," he pointed upstairs to the twins' bedroom.

"I don't want your right arm." She pushed her chair back, to be farther away from him. "And this changes everything."

"Whatever you want," he said quickly. Very quickly. "I don't blame you for wanting to leave."

Leave? Had she said she wanted to leave?

He reached across the table and took her hand. "Keep wearing your rings," he said, placing them back on her finger. "Don't upset the girls. Not yet."

"We're all done," I tell her. "Except for mascara. Open your eyes, Miss."

I put her purse on the floor so I can remove her cape. "You can put the rings back on now," I tell Murphy. "The polish is dry." But Murphy doesn't make a move. I turn her around so she can see her hair and make-up in the mirror. I maybe went a little overboard on the mascara, possibly, because now her eyes are actually kind of watery, like she's about to cry.

She holds her hands out in front of her—even I can't believe how good they look. Snowflakes on her fingers and toes but still she doesn't say anything.

"Look in the mirror, Miss," I tell her. "When you get home tonight your husband will think he's in the wrong house. Your husband won't know you."

"You're right, Valerie. I'm sure there will be quite a surprise waiting for him at home."

"And that's good, right?"

"It's for the best." She looks right at me and stands up real straight.

Now Murphy holds her left hand out in front of her, admiring her manicure. This is a good thing. It helps keep the polish from getting damaged since it's still so fresh, and besides, that little red circle needs air. ◇

Hatchling

John Thomas Murphy

W E ALL KNEW THE MEXICAN KID COLLECTED TURTLES, BUT I was the only one who found out he was not an actual Mexican. It was the day after the playground brawl when Frank's dad beat the hell out of Jack's dad. I left the house early that morning, both Mom and Dad dead asleep (her: bed; him: couch). The whole neighborhood was quiet. No parents anywhere. That wasn't the case the night before, when the bonfire and the drunks raged.

The kids weren't out, either, so I walked through the McGlicks' backyard until I reached the path to the woods. After a few hundred yards, I entered a small clearing. I listened to the stream trickle as it meandered underneath the rotting footbridge. Squirrels spiraled up trees, and I heard two dogs bark in the distance. As I walked deeper into the woods, I almost didn't notice him standing next to the stream.

The Mexican kid. Next to his feet lay a small tub. I slowly walked up to him, and he kept his head down for a long minute.

"Hatchlings," he said. I thought this was some weird Mexican word. I shrugged.

"Hatchling turtles," he repeated, pointing into the tub.

Two tiny turtles paddled in the water, one scrambling to climb onto a rock.

"Hatchling turtles?"

"I found them by the road," the Mexican kid said.

"What were they doing by the road?"

144

"Beats me. Maybe they wandered off. If they have no other turtles to look out for them, they'll die. So my father makes me bring them back here."

"You're always walking around with turtles," I said.

"Yeah, I have some at home. But not little ones like this. My father would kill me."

"I'm Mike," I said.

"Salvador," said the Mexican kid, nodding.

"Did you just come here from Mexico?"

"Nope, we moved up here from the Bronx. That's where I grew up. And my parents are Dominican, not Mexican."

I tilted my head at him. "Can I hold a turtle?"

Salvador stepped in front of the turtles. "You'll hurt them. They're very fragile."

For the first time, I looked at Salvador and really saw his face. He had the darkest green eyes I'd ever seen. His lips were pale and small, and his nose formed a perfect triangle.

"How do you know I'd hurt them?"

"You just don't know what you're doing."

The Mexican kid thought I was dumb? The Mexican kid? He was the punch line of the neighborhood jokes. Piñata this, donkey that, sombrero here, burrito there.

Then I said it: "They're only stupid turtles, anyway. I should come back tonight and kill them all."

Salvador's green eyes tightened. Their sadness changed into a dangerous fury. "If you kill them, I'll kill you."

I ran a few steps away. "I'm getting my brother and my cousin. Then we'll see who kills who." My voice was more of a shriek than a threat.

I peeked over my shoulder and saw Salvador, head bowed, looking down into the tub. With every step, my anger rose. I'd get Tommy and Bugs. Then I'd get Frank and Jack. After their dads' brawl, they'd be ready to jump Salvador. I pictured kicking Salvador in the head over and over while the boys held him down. I wanted to stomp on his turtles in front of him.

Eventually I reached the street, where the boys were now playing football. I ran panting up to them. My brother Tommy looked in my direction and spat on the ground.

"You can't play," he said. "You missed out 'cuz you went on your little nature walk."

"But you don't understand."

"I understand just fine—there's no room for you. Don't you have doll time now?"

Some of the other boys laughed, and my face reddened. I played with stuffed bears until I was seven, and my brother never let me hear the end of it.

"I don't play with dolls," I said. "I'm not a little kid anymore."

"You're not? Then since you're such a big boy, maybe you can go watch another episode of Dora the Explorer."

More laughter. I picked up a thin rock and chucked it at Tommy, but it curved away and skipped along the street. Afraid of him battering me into the ground, I sprinted back toward the woods.

I slowed down when I knew he wasn't behind me and continued toward the stream. When I began to hear the water dribbling along, I saw Salvador sitting on a log. The tub was between his feet, and he was splashing a stick around in the water. He didn't look up, but when I was closer, Salvador spoke.

"I made a nest for them. I think the turtles in the stream will help." I saw that the tub was empty of turtles. I couldn't look him in the eye.

"I was hoping to be your friend," he said. "I haven't made any friends since moving up here."

"I wasn't really gonna have all of them beat you up," I lied.

"I know," said Salvador.

We were silent. The birds whistled. I snuck a peek at Salvador and noticed he was lost in thought. I imagined that he was dreaming about mythical lands where he could save the endangered, people and animals alike. The woods were peaceful. I closed my eyes and pictured Salvador wearing a green shell as a crown. The king of the turtles.

"Do you want to come back and check out some of the bigger

turtles at my house?" he asked.

"Sure," I said.

On the walk home, the neighborhood was more alive. The fathers, drunk the night before, now sipped coffee on their front porches. We heard playful yelling in the distance, and, as the sun grew hot overhead, we went into the Mexican kid's house, walked down to his dark basement, and watched a bunch of turtles live their quiet lives. ◇

Liberated

Lisa Romano Licht

Twenty-seven and hog-tied by the wrong love,
I break free.
Friends (having weddings, having babies)
Forget to catch me
As I fall backwards,
Too busy asking each other:
What is she waiting for?

I visit the house on Seymour Avenue
Where my grandmother hears my story;
Familiar walls regard me,
Close our space of fifty years.

We flank her kitchen sink,
Her glistening, wrinkled hands
Rinse a fleshy tomato;
My young, tanned fingers
Brush yesterday's rose petals,
Slightly bruised,
In the window jar.

I stand at the speckled Formica counter,
Worn by the rub of her hands on wax paper
Sprinkling cheese into meat,
Bathing chicken in bread crumbs,
Prelude to thousands of dinners
Served thousands of nights
On the same plates to my grandfather.

My words slow to a drip, then run dry.
She wipes her hands on the faded *mappina**
And tells me
What no diamond-blinded friend would:
"You need to do
What will make you happy."

Her name was Adele.
She left Italy alone when she was seventeen.
She said the Rosary every day.
If you asked her what kind of soda she wanted
She would say, "Whatever's open."
She lived to ninety-six with her husband.

When I was falling backwards,
She gave me her kitchen chair. ◇

**dishtowel*

Nexus

Lisa Romano Licht

Standing on Disney's *faux* sidewalk
Where streetlamps deny
Ink spilled across the sky,
I make a selfish memory.

Not for my girls, two and five, whose
Excitement flares and wanes,
Fueled by a flurry of silver balloons—
Fleeting.

The intoxication is mine.
While swarms of strangers swell
Around me,
My two families surround me:

The husband
I had luck enough to wait for,
The children, unfinished proof
Of our stumblings and shinings

And the matrix that shaped me—
Mother, father and brother—
Witness to my younger incarnations
Shared at the kitchen table.

We make our collective way to the curb;
White starbursts, then blue, decorate
The night, shower the castle
With ghostly light.

As their faces read the illustrated sky,
I see them true,
Visceral in my love for their
Flawed perfection.

I stand apart, complete. ◇

Cleopatra's Choice

Gloria Lazar

First day of spring, snowflakes,
like Octavius Caesar's troops
invading Egypt, threaten
buds of violet crocus,
fragile shoots of daffodil,
hedonist spring straining
to bring rich tints
to a charcoal sketch.

The sky brightens and still
the snow continues, persistent
troops intent on destroying
Cleopatra, who will take
the asp's bite rather than
surrender to cruel Rome.

If you had waited, Cleopatra,
rather than assuming slavery,
hoping for time and your charms
to sway cunning Octavius,
you might have risen again
and walked with majesty,
fields of green beneath your feet,
fragrance of peonies and roses
like an ermine cloak
trailing behind you. ◇

Purifying
the Planet

Bill Maynard

I'M OFF TO WORK IN MY GARDEN," I TOLD HER.

"Ah yes," she sneered, "your mysterious garden." She turned away and her expression of contempt was multiplied on the stainless steel pots that were strung in a row above her stove. It leaped from pot to pot to coffee maker to toaster until her whole kitchen watched me with hostile eyes.

She withdrew a blade from the cluster stabbed deep in a wood block and began to dissect an avocado. "And where might this so-called garden be?"

A fair question, I thought, since our apartment building was firmly anchored in seamless macadam.

"Not far," I assured her.

"There are things that need doing right here," she complained, "not that you'd ever be inclined to help."

"I won't be going back after today."

"Then perhaps you might be on time for dinner just once before everything I've cooked is cold."

I slipped her orange-handled scissors into a dark plastic bag and left.

FINDING THE PROPER SOIL hadn't been easy. The refineries spewed forth pollution, but not the right kind. The pig farms were disgusting but also inadequate. Eventually I discovered a spongy patch, roughly ten-by-ten, between two froth-covered pools not far from the Turnpike. An abandoned brick building, the glass smashed from its windows, darkened the ground with shadow. Perfect, I thought.

"I hope you're not planning to dig there," a passing scavenger warned on the day I approached with a spade. "They made wood preservatives until it became illegal a few years ago."

TO OBTAIN STARTER PLANTS from the EPA I had to dream up a project and promise to keep records. When I approached my plot carrying flats of fresh green shoots, a man in a gray security uniform stood in my way.

"What the hell do you think you're doing?" he asked.

"I'm purifying the planet," I told him.

"With plants?"

"*Pteris vittata*," I replied. "A tropical fern with highly unusual properties."

"I'd wear gloves if I were you. You're digging in some highly unusual dirt."

AND NOW—FINALLY—harvest time. As I approached from a high point on the Turnpike, my patch of green stood out from the uniform grayness as if it were unexpected life as viewed from a moon-lander. Drawing closer, I watched my plants bend and sway in the breezes churned up by the eighteen-wheelers as they rocketed by. I snipped the ferns into four-inch segments and placed them gently in the plastic bag. Greenish yellow, plump and juicy, they were brimming with arsenic they had absorbed from the soil.

"WHAT A PAIN IN THE ASS YOU ARE," she said, as I reentered our apartment. She sat at the kitchen table, a glass of wine in her hand, Dr. Phil on the screen, secure in her lair. "Selfish, thoughtless, inconsiderate," she continued. "Always too late and today too damned early. I haven't even begun to cook."

"I'll make the salad," I volunteered. ◇

155

CONTRIBUTORS

Seth Appel resides in Scarsdale with his wife, Hana, and their two children, Azumi and Viggo.

Debra Banerjee is Arts and Entertainment editor for *The Scarsdale Inquirer.* She had a short story in the first volume of *The Westchester Review* and has written for *Greenwich Magazine, India Abroad,* and *Arthritis Health Monitor* magazine. Interviewing Cynthia Ozick was one of the highlights of her career in journalism.

Marlena Maduro Baraf was born in Panama. While she has studied and worked and raised a family in the United States, her favorite place—still—is a hammock by the sea. She lives in Scarsdale. with her husband.

Jessica Bennett lives in Katonah, with her patient husband, their two teenagers, and a coonhound.

Rosetta Benson has two loves: poetry and art. In May 2008 she received an MFA in Creative Writing from Queens University, Charlotte, N.C. When she is not writing, she volunteers as a docent at the Katonah Museum of Art.

Kristina Bicher is a graduate of Manhattanville College (MAW program) and Harvard College. She lives in Rye with her very supportive family and can often be found digging in the dirt when not involved with various community groups.

A. H. Block, a retiree from thirty-five years in TV prodution, intermixes writing with volunteering, reading, and puttering. His poetry and prose have appeared in well over two dozen publications. He lives with his wife in Bronxville, and, though they have successfully grown peas and tomatoes, they've never attempted corn.

Mary Lou Butler-Buschi lives in Larchmont. Her work has appeared in *The Laurel Review, Indiana Review, Southern Indiana Review, Babel Fruit,* and *Italian Americana,* among others. Mary Lou is also a NYC Teaching Fellow currently working with children with autism.

David Carlyon—Army vet, ex-Ringling Bros. and Barnum & Bailey Circus clown, and Equity actor—has a Berkeley JD and a Northwestern PhD. He won Westchester's

Washington Irving Award for his book *Dan Rice: The Most Famous Man You've Never Heard Of*. He's married to the Broadway producer Barbara Whitman.

Mark Deitch is a member of the Hudson Valley Writers Center and recipient of the 2009 James J. Nicholson Political Poetry Prize. He lives in Ossining, with his wife, Diane, and has attended several hundred baseball and softball games played by his son, Josh, and daughter, Ariel.

Lisa Fleck Dondiego lives in Ossining and writes poetry. She's a member of the Poetry Caravan and the Hudson Valley Writers' Center, and won first prize in the 2008 Town of Greenburgh Poetry Contest. She has read her poems throughout Westchester and at the Cornelia Street Café in Greenwich Village.

Kevin Egan, of White Plains, is the author of five novels. His short fiction has appeared in *Rosebud, Alfred Hitchcock Mystery Magazine,* and *Fiction Quarterly*. He teaches fiction writing as an adjunct instructor at Westchester Community College.

Lee Eiferman is a short-story writer and screenwriter living in Westchester with her family and frisky dog. Her short stories have been published by *Top Stories* and *Between C&D*. Her numerous screenplays have placed as finalists in screenplay competitions. She continues to write every day.

Lya Ferreyra is fifteen years old, a tenth-grader at Rye Neck High School, and a member of the *Scholastic* Kids Press Corps. She hopes to become a writer, but if that doesn't work out, she plans to be an editor for a publishing company.

Judith Naomi Fish has been a Westchester journalist for twenty years. Her fiction and personal essays have appeared in regional and national publications.

Lesleigh Forsyth is an editor of *The Westchester Review*. Her poems have been published in *Nimrod, Rattapallax, Lumina, The Sarah Lawrence Review,* and *Big City Lit,* and in *Grief and the Healing Arts* (Baywood Publishers, 1999). She is an active amateur cellist and lives in Larchmont.

Denise Mozilo Frasca is a teacher. Several of her poems are published in *Mother/Daughter Duets*, a book about adult daughter/mother relationships. In 2008, she received the James Nicholson Political Poetry Award for her poem "Memorial Day." She was a selected poet for Poets and Writers on War and Peace.

Jacqueline Grandsire Goldstein, now retired, taught high school English in the Bronx for many years. Since retiring from teaching she has been studying at the Writing Institute at Sarah Lawrence College.

Joseph P. Griffith is a writer and editor who lives in Yonkers. He has written for *The New York Times,* published four nonfiction books, and won awards for writing and design. He is the author of several legitimate and illegitimate works of fiction, including some screenplays seeking a home.

Adrienne Hernandez's poems have appeared in the *Mid-America Poetry Review* and various small presses. She has facilitated intergenerational poetry writing workshops and is a member of the Poetry Caravan.

Gloria Lazar is a poet and writer in Tarrytown. In 2009, her poetry was performed at the Hudson Valley Center for Contemporary Art as part of *The Form of Matter* and published in *The Form of Matter Journal of Poetry*. Her work has appeared in previous volumes of *The Westchester Review*.

Linda Levitz works in the special education department of the local elementary school in Ardsley. Her poems have appeared in numerous journals. She is the author of three collections of poetry: *Trusting the Stones, The Dark Face of Planting,* and *Directions to My House*.

Steven Lewis teaches writing at Empire State College and The Writing Institute at Sarah Lawrence College. His most recent books are *Fear and Loathing of Boca Raton* and *A Month on a Barrier Island*. Please visit *www.stevelewiswriter.com* for a more complete publishing history.

Lisa Romano Licht is pursuing her Master of Arts in Writing at Manhattanville College. Her poem "Nexus" and her story "The Order of Things" were Top 25 finalists in *Writer's Digest's* Writing Competitions for 2008. A long-time Westchester resident, she now lives in Rockland with her husband and two daughters.

Bill Maynard lives in Larchmont with his wife, Marilyn, their collie, Missy, and their golden retriever, Casey. His previous books, written for his seven grandchildren, include *Incredible Ned, Quiet,Wyatt!, Santa's Time Off, Rock River,* and *Pondfire*.

Elizabeth Meaney is an alumna of the University of Notre Dame and lives in Mamaroneck. Her poetry has appeared in *Xenith, The Furnace Review, The Literary Bohemian,* and *Cicada Magazine*. Her first novel, *Bloodthirsty*, will be published under the name "Flynn Meaney" by Little, Brown this fall.

John Thomas Murphy's work has appeared in many journals, such as *Quarter After Eight, The Oak Bend Review, JMWW,* and *The Cortland Review*. He holds degrees from the University of Pennsylvania and SUNY-New Paltz, where he won the Tomaselli Creative Writing Award in 2001. He can be reached at *johnthomasmurphywriter @gmail.com*.

By the time **Gunter Nitsch,** the author of *Weeds Like Us,* was thirteen years old, he had lived in Nazi Germany, in Soviet Russia, and in a refugee camp in West

Germany. Formerly of Scarsdale, he now lives in Chicago, where he is writing a sequel to his memoir.

Alana Ruprecht holds a BA from Lewis & Clark College and an MFA in Creative Writing from Lesley University. This is her first publication.

Thaddeus Rutkowski grew up in central Pennsylvania and is the author of the novels *Tetched* and *Roughhouse*. Both books were finalists for an Asian American Literary Award. He teaches at the Writer's Voice of the West Side YMCA in Manhattan and at City University of New York

Natalie Safir has had poems in the journals *Slant, Pivot, MidAmerican Review, Rhino, Natural Bridge, ForPoetry.com* and ezines, since the 1980s and anthologized in college texts. Her collections: *Moving into Seasons, To Face the Inscription, Made Visible, A Clear Burning. Love like Snow* is forthcoming in 2010.

This is the third story that **Stanley Sokol** has published. He is currently working on his third novel, which is set in White Plains, his home for the past twenty-two years.

Joanna Valente lives and writes in New York. She often wears large glasses and bakes cupcakes. Currently, she is completing her bachelor's degree in Creative Writing and Literature at SUNY Purchase College. In the future, she would like to live by the ocean and own too many cats.

Elisabeth von Uhl graduated in May 2005 with an MFA from Sarah Lawrence College. She now teaches composition at Fordham University. Her work has been published in *Lumina, The Broome Review, Moria, CrossBronx,* and *The Cortland Review.* Her chapbook, *Ocean Sea,* is published by Finishing Line Press.

Catherine Wald, a freelance writer and native of Westchester, is the author of *The Resilient Writer: 23 Tales of Rejection and Triumph* (Persea, 2004).

Dale Walkonen is a poet, mime, and playwright who lives in New Rochelle. She is a graduate of Sarah Lawrence College and Boston University, where she studied with Jane Cooper and Anne Sexton. She has taught at Concordia College, College of New Rochelle, and Sacred Heart University.

Missy Egan Wey is a member of the National League of American PEN Women. She earned a Master's Degree in Writing from Manhattanville College and is a founding member of the Dowd-O'Gorman Writing Center. Her poetry has been published in literary journals including *INKWELL, Crucible, Eureka,* and *The Westchester Review.*

Kathleen Williamson has lived her whole adult life in Westchester. She currently lives in Pleasantville, with her husband and two children. She is a founding member of the Pleasantville Special Education PTA.

Peter Wood is an English teacher at White Plains High School. His two books, *A Clenched Fist: The Making of a Champion* and *Confessions of a Fighter: Battling Through the Golden Gloves,* were published by Ringside Books this spring.

SUPPORTERS

Louise Albert
Dr. David Albert
James Barush
Elizabeth Blagg
Mary and Steve Borowka
Susan Duncan
Mindy and Andrew Feldman
Sandy and George Gottlieb
RoseAnn and George Hermann
Jean Katzenberg
Charlotte W. Krinsly
Jocelyn S. Reznick
Joelyn Rohman
Libby Saines
Martin Sarullo
Ann and Paul Spindel
Kathryn and Mark Spindel
Dr. Robert Spitzer
Sheila and Burton Stone
Dr. Allen M. Terdiman
Dr. Jonathan P. Terdiman
Dr. Madhulika G. Varma
Janet Williams, D.S.W.
Rick Wingate
Elaine K. Winik

Anonymous

BOOKSELLERS
Anderson's Book Shop
  Larchmont, N.Y.
Arcade Booksellers
  Rye, N.Y.
Galápagos Books
  Hastings-on-Hudons, N.Y.
Reading Writing & Wrapping
  Scarsdale, N.Y.
The Village Book Shop
  Bronxville, N.Y.
Womrath Book Shop
  Bronxville, N.Y.

OTHER MERCHANTS
Designer One
  Larchmont, N.Y.
Futterman's Stationery
  Larchmont, N.Y.
Silver Tips Tea Room
  Tarrytown, N.Y.
Truly yours, Kelly!
  Tuckahoe, N.Y.

PAST CONTRIBUTING AUTHORS

Lisa Argrette Ahmad ◆ Floyd Albert ◆ Harley April ◆ Ze'ev Aviezer
Debra Banerjee ◆ Donna Barkman ◆ Alex Barnett ◆ Jessica Bennett
Rosetta Benson ◆ Sally Bliumis-Dunn ◆ Steve Cain ◆ Rod Carlson
Liane Kupferberg Carter ◆ Linda Hillman Chayes ◆ Llyn Clague
Stephanie Kaplan Cohen ◆ Patrick Conley ◆ Judy Coulter
Lisa Fleck Dondiego ◆ Ted Davis ◆ P. J. DeGenaro ◆ Arlene Edelson
Kevin Egan ◆ Sara Fasy ◆ D. A. Feinfeld ◆ Sheila Filipowski
Judith Naomi Fish ◆ Katherine Flaherty ◆ Lesleigh Forsyth
Patrica Anne Frame ◆ Eleanor Gaffney ◆ Nina Gabriele-Cuva
Kate M. Gallagher ◆ Campbell Geeslin ◆ Diane Germano ◆ Sophie Glass
Myrna Goodman ◆ Blythe Hamer ◆ Ruth D. Handel ◆ Lu Hauser
David Hellerstein ◆ Jack Hickey ◆ Catherine Hiller ◆ Susan Hodara
Luann Jacobs ◆ Kuniko Katz ◆ Jean Katzenberg ◆ Karen Kawaguchi
Autumn Kindelspire ◆ Stephen Kling ◆ Nathan Kolodney
Florence Reiss Kraut ◆ Joe Landau ◆ Janice Landrum ◆ Gloria Lazar
Meg Lindsay ◆ Pei-Ling Lue ◆ Julia Mallach ◆ Rich Manley ◆ Eve Marx
Maura McCaw ◆ Merle Molofsky ◆ Joan Motyka ◆ J. Mullee
Ruth Obernbreit ◆ Zachary Pace ◆ Sharon Medoff Picard ◆ Kevin Pilkington
Holly Posner ◆ Royal F. Potter ◆ Ross Priel ◆ Jeff Queen ◆ Paul-John Ramos
Jocelyn Reznick ◆ Natalie Safir ◆ Boria Sax ◆ Bill Scher ◆ Steven Schnur
Cora Schwartz ◆ Amy Ralston Seife ◆ Emily Seife ◆ Ruth Seldin
Galit and Gilad Seliktar ◆ Ilene Semiatin ◆ Roberta Silman
Rachel M. Simon ◆ Linda Simone ◆ Jena Smith ◆ Stanley Sokol
Gloria Donen Sosin ◆ Todd Strasser ◆ Barry Roark Strutt ◆ Laurie Sullivan
Allen M. Terdiman ◆ Meredith Trede ◆ Sergio Troncoso ◆ Les Von Losberg
Betty Wald ◆ Jeff Wanshel ◆ James L. Weil ◆ Barbara Weinreb
Missy Egan Wey ◆ Tracy P. Williamson ◆ Hilton Wilson ◆ Rachel Wineberg
Elaine K. Winik ◆ Amelia B. Winkler ◆ Mark Wisniewski ◆ Catherine Wolf
Elizabeth Wood ◆ Joyce Zaritsky ◆ Judy Zendell